SKILL & SHOOTING POCKET BOOK

Author: Major (Retd) John Hobbis Harris

Designed, Produced and Published by
Military Pocket Books Ltd

ISBN 1-874528-06-3

British Library Cataloguing in Publication Data
A catalogue record for this book is available from the British Library

The Cover Design is from an original water colour by the late Richard Scollins, Ilkeston, Derby, subsequently updated by Carl Marshall, Artist and Illustrator, Nottingham.
The 'ghost' figures on the cover represent - from left to right:
A Private - Light Coy, Bethnal Green Vols 1798.
A Rifle Vol of 1860.
A member of the Imperial Yeomanry 1900.
An Infantry Private of 'Kitcheners' Army 1916.
A Paratrooper circa 1960's

PO Box 28, Leven, Beverley
East Yorkshire HU17 5 LA UK
Tel & Fax (44) 01964 - 542878
Log on to: www. milpkbk.co.uk

A Rifleman circa 1750's of the 15th Regiment of Foot, The EastYorkshire Regiment (The Snappers)

CONTENT

PAGE No

Acknowledgements

The Publishers would like to thank HQ Land Command for the use of photographs and HQ ARA (Army Rifle Association) for the information on Skill At Arms Meetings and Match conditions.

SAFETY PRECAUTIONS
RULES FOR HANDLING WEAPONS OF ANY TYPE AT ALL TIMES

1. Whenever you pick up a weapon, or have a weapon handed to you or when you take over a weapon, ALWAYS carry out the NORMAL SAFETY PRECAUTIONS (NSP). Whether it is your own or someone else's weapon, ALWAYS examine it to ensure that it is NOT loaded.
2. NEVER point a weapon at anyone - even in fun.
3. ALWAYS handle a weapon so that it points in a direction that there is NO DANGER if a round is accidentally fired.
4. NEVER rest the muzzle of a loaded weapon, or a weapon 'made safe' on your foot or against your body. Similarly, do not hold a weapon with your hand or hands placed over the muzzle.
5. Weapons will NEVER be carried in VEHICLES either loaded or in a 'made safe' state; operational conditions excepted.
6. YOU will NOT fire any weapon until such time as you have been fully trained, exercised and tested to be capable of safely handling the weapon.
7. When handing over a weapon to someone else, SHOW/PROVE to them first that it is in a SAFE and in an UNLOADED state.
8. When anyone hands a weapon to you: NO MATTER WHO THEY ARE - *INSIST* THAT THEY SHOW/PROVE IT TO YOU.
9. NO weapon will be tampered with to make modifications etc., severe action will be taken against anyone doing this.

"IT'S BETTER TO BE SAFE THAN SORRY"

TECHNICAL DATA

AMMUNITION	**5.56 RIFLE**	**LSW**
Calibre (mm)	5.56 mm	
Types	Both weapons Ball, Tracer, Blank.	
Weight of Round (g)	12 g.	
MECHANICAL FEATURES		
Firing Modes	Single Shot & Automatic	
Methods of Operation	Gas and Spring	
Locking	Rotary Bolt, Forward Locking	
Feed	Magazine (30 rounds)	
FIRING CHARACTERISTICS		
Muzzle Velocity (m/s)	940 m/s	970 m/s
Recoil (joules)	4 j	
Number of Barrel Grooves	4	
Pitch of Rifling (mm)	1 Turn in 175	
Twist of Rifling	Right Hand	
SIGHTING		
Optical Sight (SUSAT)	Sight Unit Small Arms Trilux	
Magnification	x 4	
Field of View (mils)	177 mils	
Eye Relief (mm)	24 mm	
Range Setting (metres)	300 to 800	
Iron Sight		
Foresight	Post	
Backsight	Twin Apertures	
Sight Radius (mm)	290 to 320 mm	
Range (metres)	Up to 300	
WEIGHTS (kg)		
With SUSAT and Full Magazine	5.08 kg	6.88 kg
Weapon only	3.8 kg	5.6 kg
Magazine with 30 Rounds	0.48	
Magazine empty	0.12	
SUSAT	0.8	
Iron Sight	0.3	
Bayonet and Scabbard	0.3	
LENGTHS (mm)		
Weapon	780 mm	900 mm
Bayonet	300 mm	
Rifle with Bayonet Fixed	980 mm	

SKILL AT ARMS

INTRODUCTION

The 5.56 Rifle and the Light Support Weapon have the same basic components and therefore most parts are interchangeable. In view of this fact when ever possible we refer to it as the 'weapon'

The LSW differs from the Rifle in having a LONGER BARREL, an OUTRIGGER with a BIPOD, a smaller front HAND GUARD, a small rear HAND GRIP on the BUTT and a SHOULDER STRAP, as illustrated on the next page. The recent technical modifications made to the weapon have met with the approval of those who use it.

Both weapons use a short stroke gas operated system and a rotary forward-locking breech mechanism to give either single shot or automatic operation from a 30 round MAGAZINE. The weapon is designed to be fired from the RIGHT shoulder only.

On the 5.56 Rifle, the 22mm diameter FLASH ELIMINATOR enables the firing of rifle grenades, using a GRENADE LAUNCHER. The Rifle is your personal weapon; with it you must become highly skilled to handle every situation in which a you may find yourself. Above all, you must handle the weapons safely at all times.

The tactical advantage of the weapon and its capability of firing single rounds or bursts, is in producing :-

a. Quick, accurate fire at short range opportunity targets.

b. A high rate of accurate controlled fire at longer ranges.

c. Effective section fire power at ranges up to 600 metres.

There are two sighting systems for the weapons, the fully optical SUSAT (Sight Unit Small Arms Trilux) and/or an IRON SIGHT, comprising a FORESIGHT and a BACK SIGHT incorporated in the carrying handle. The basic weapon can be stripped down into seven major groups as shown on the next page.

Further stripping of some groups is possible and in some circumstances may be required for cleaning or replacing damaged or worn parts.

Safety Precaution Drills are dealt with in later pages, but before handling the weapon your instructor will carry out the Normal Safety Precautions.

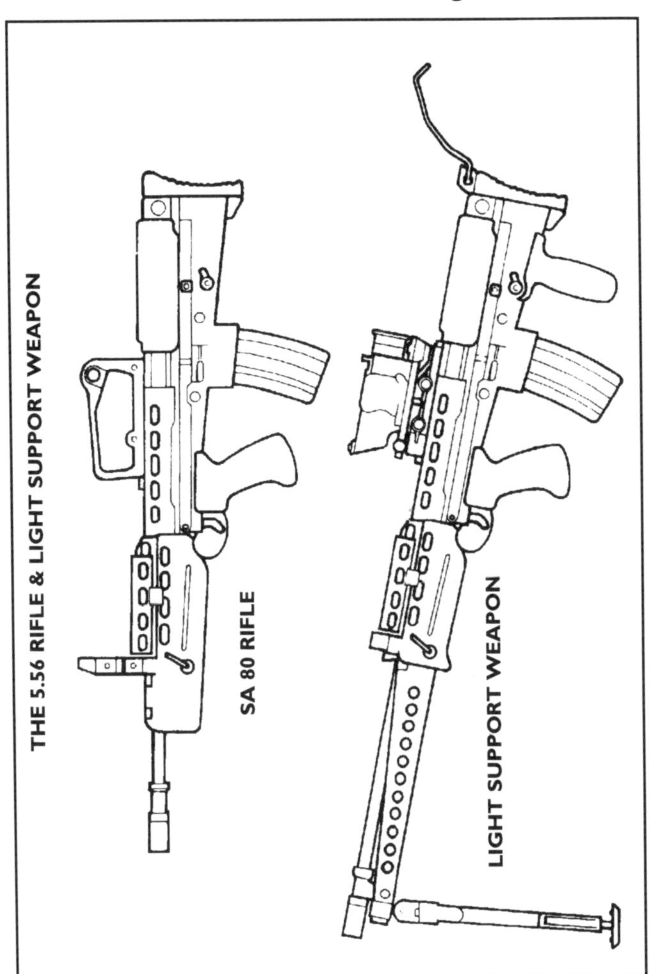
THE 5.56 RIFLE & LIGHT SUPPORT WEAPON
SA 80 RIFLE
LIGHT SUPPORT WEAPON

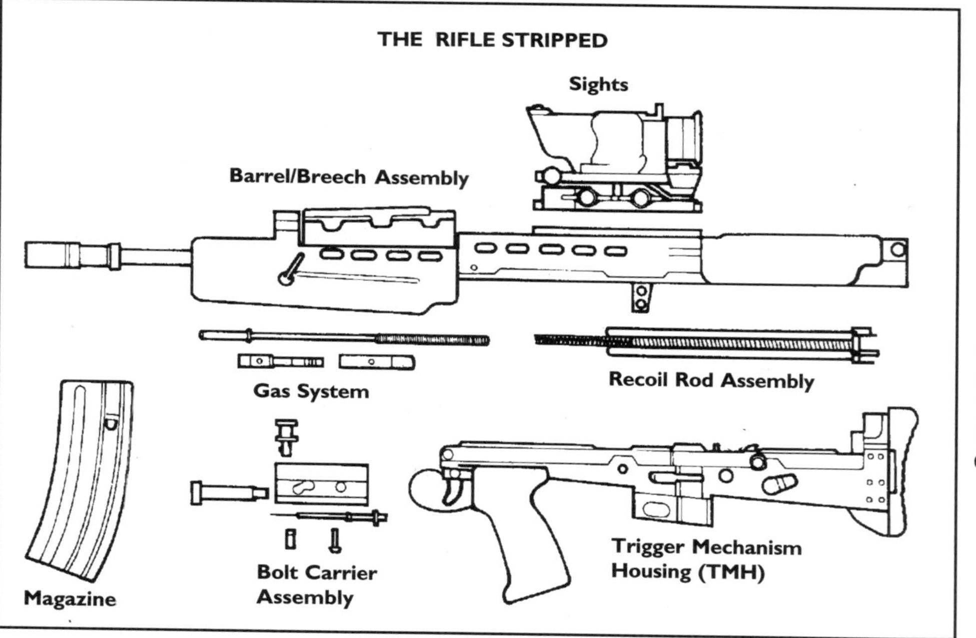
THE RIFLE STRIPPED
Sights
Barrel/Breech Assembly
Gas System
Recoil Rod Assembly
Magazine
Bolt Carrier
Assembly
Trigger Mechanism
Housing (TMH)

Skill at Arms & Shooting

HANDLING

WEAPON CONTROLS - see below..

This illustrates the physical position of the weapon controls.

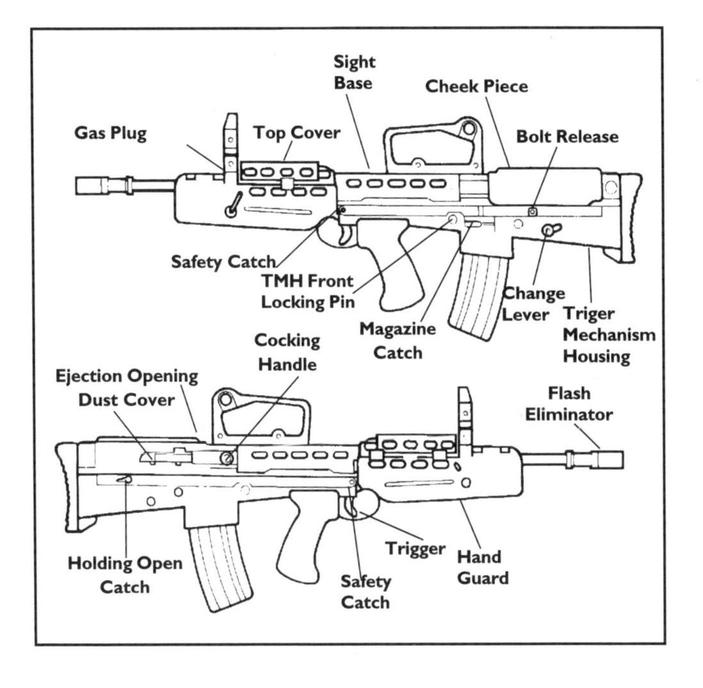

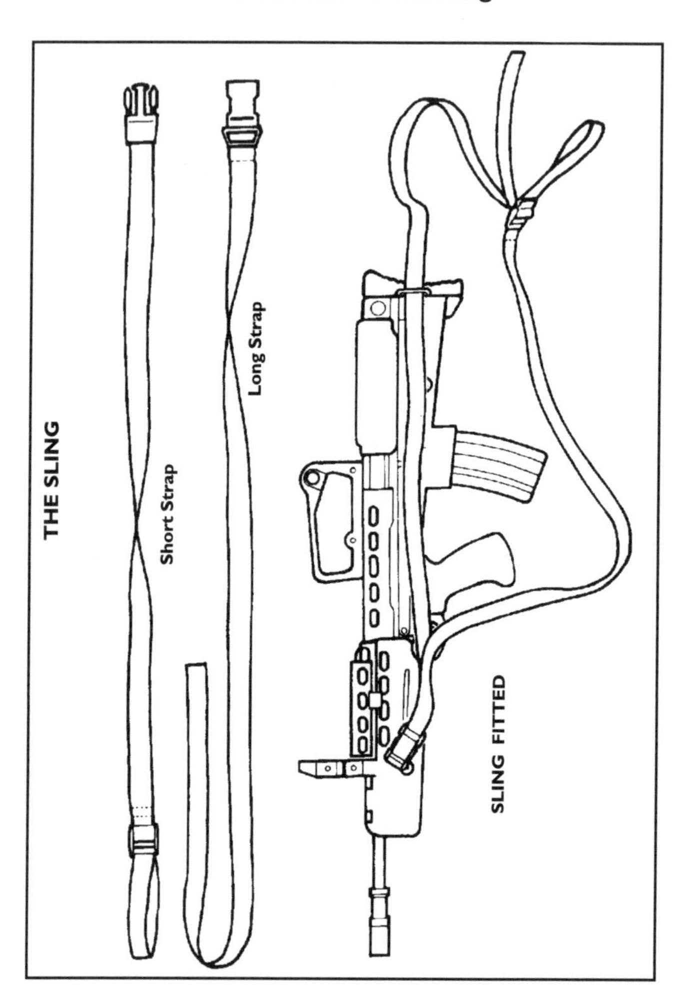
THE SLING
Short Strap
Long Strap
SLING FITTED

ACCESSORIES & SPARES

Additional items listed below, are not necessarily essential to fire the weapon, but their use and application are explained in the following paragraphs:-

The Sling. The Bayonet & Scabbard.
The Blank Firing Attachment. The Tool Roll & Spare Parts.

The SLING - see the illustrations on following pages - is made of two lengths of webbing type material, which link together with a special quick release BUCKLE CLIP.

The first longer piece has at one end a female part of the clip and a flat plastic loop attached, the other end of the strap is clear.

The second shorter piece has the male part of the clip at one end, and the quick release buckle and loop at the other.

Fitting the Sling **see illustrations 1 to 6 over page.**

1. Take the longer strap and lay it flat along the weapon, with the FEMALE CLIP end towards the MUZZLE and the flat plastic loop pointing outwards. Feed the clear end through the FRONT SLING LOOP and then through the FLAT PLASTIC LOOP on the strap. Pull tight.
2. Take the SHORTER strap and, holding it parallel with the first strap and with the MALE clip end pointing outwards, feed the clear end of the LONGER strap through and over the RIDGED EDGE of the gate in the base of the male clip on the SHORT strap, connect the male and female parts of the clip together.
3. Ensure that the LONGER strap remains untwisted, then feed the CLEAR end through the REAR SLING LOOP on the weapon.
4. Check that the SHORTER strap is not twisted, then feed the clear end of the LONGER strap outwards through the main gate of the BUCKLE BAR.
5. Finally, thread the CLEAR END of the LONGER strap through the gate in the BUCKLE. TO REMOVE the SLING, reverse the fitting procedure as above.

USES OF THE SLING Essentially the SLING can be used in two ways, although other variations may be possible.

FRONT SLUNG POSITION. Separate the two straps and insert your head, right arm and shoulder through the loop so formed. The weapon will now be suspended from your left shoulder across your chest. Adjust the position of the weapon by pulling down on the CLEAR end of the LONGER strap. Pulling the QUICK RELEASE loop or releasing the CLIP allows the weapon to be brought into the aim.

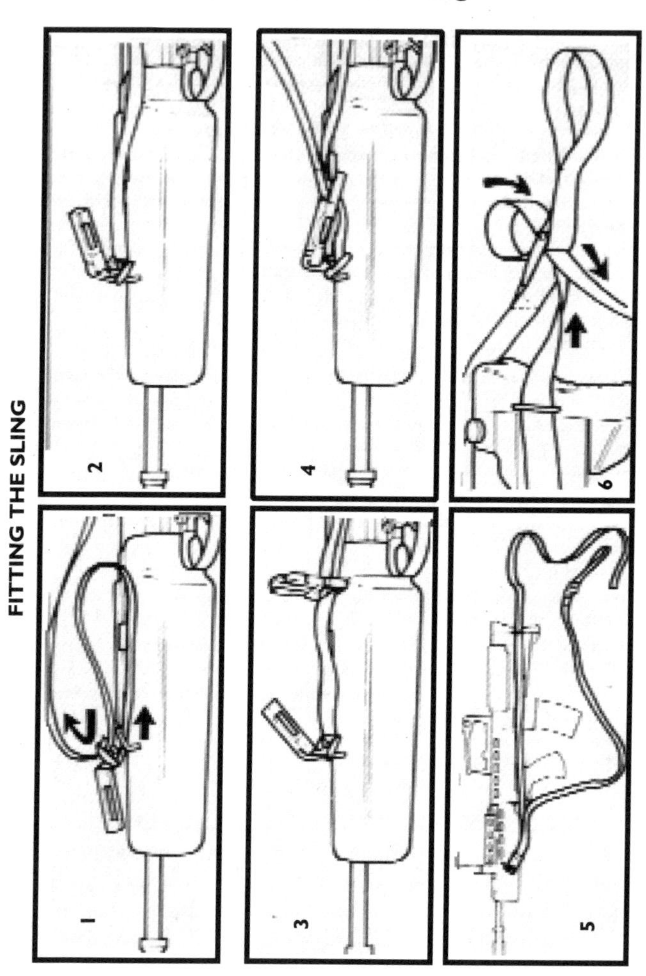
FITTING THE SLING
1
2
3
4
5
6

BACK SLUNG POSITION Separate the SLING to form TWO loops. Put an arm through each loop to position the weapon, MUZZLE down, in the centre of your back, COCKING HANDLE uppermost.

The BAYONET

The BAYONET is shaped to provide good thrust penetration. It has a cutting edge, blade channels and a ribbed portion for rope cutting. A slot at the forward end is for use with the scabbard when used as a wire cutter. The handle is shaped to enable the bayonet to be used as a fighting knife: at the rear of the handle is a release catch which secures it onto the Muzzle of the rifle. The blade end of the handle can be used as a bottle opener.

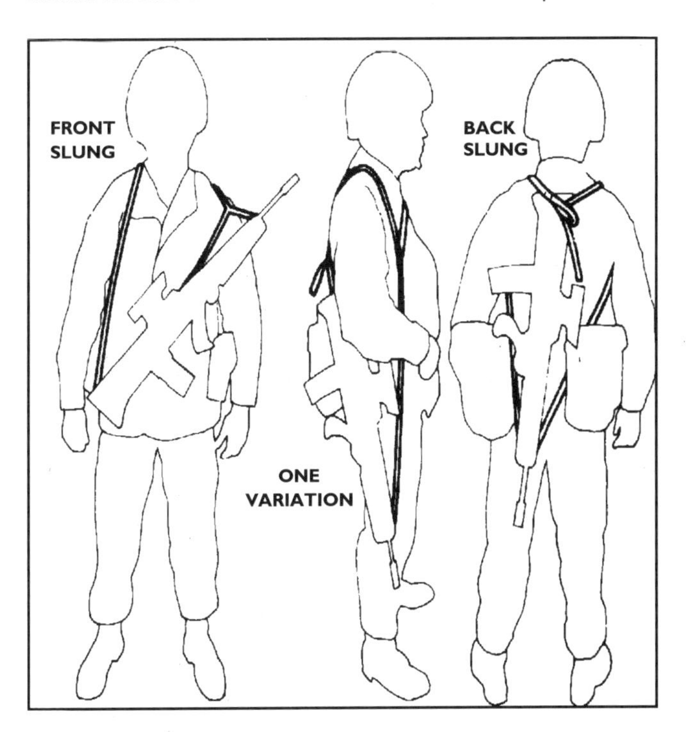

The SCABBARD is normally carried on your belt, attached by a frog or to a side of an ammunition pouch. Quick release catches are fitted.

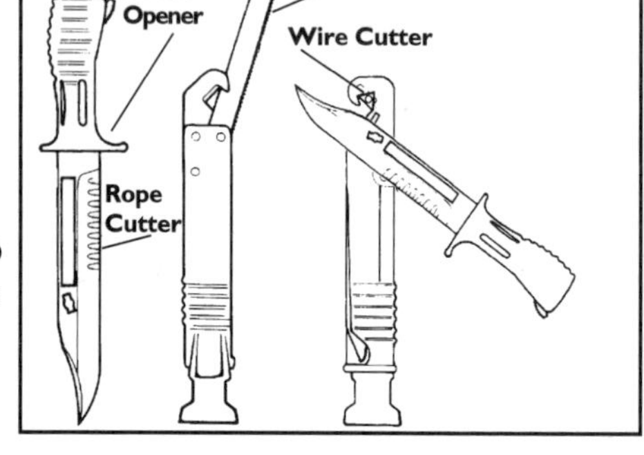

THE SCABBARD
As well as providing stowage for your BAYONET, the SCABBARD has other uses Vis:- As a SAW BLADE which unfolds from one edge of the SCABBARD and is for use on WOOD - NOT METAL.

A SHARPENING STONE integral with the opposite side of the SCABBARD. Use with light oil.

As WIRE CUTTERS by engaging the LUG of the SCABBARD with the slot in the BAYONET, ensuring that the sharp edge of the BAYONET faces away from the HOOK END of the SCABBARD.

The wedge shape on the back of the BLADE together with a corresponding hardened insert of the SCABBARD HOOK forms an effective wire-cutting device.

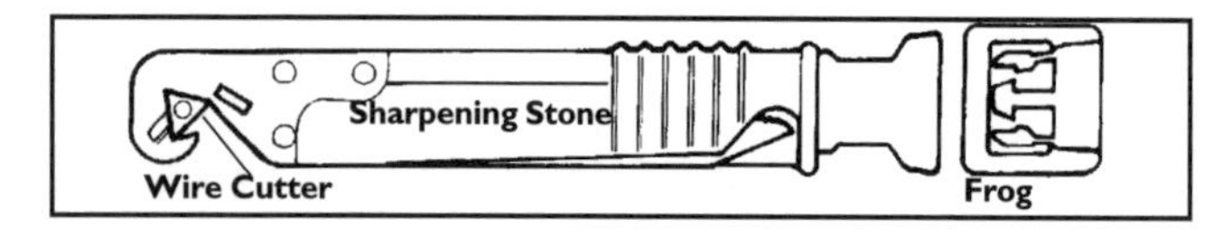

BLANK FIRING ATTACHMENT (BFA) - Fitted

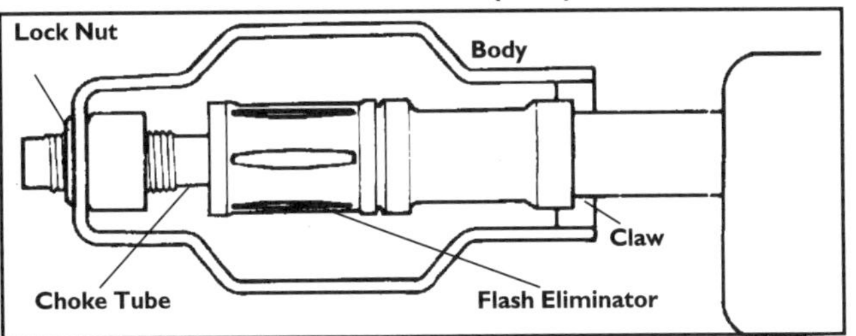

Introduction

The Blank Firing Attachment (BFA) provides a *choke or restriction* at the muzzle enabling the Rifle to operate normally when firing blank ammunition. For identification it is painted bright yellow. It may also be fitted to the LSW.

Description

The BFA BODY covers the FLASH ELIMINATOR. A CLAW at the rear clips behind the FLASH ELIMINATOR.
The CHOKE TUBE screws into the MUZZLE of the Rifle/LSW. A LOCK NUT on the TUBE locks the BFA to the BARREL.

Fitting and Removing BFA

To Fit the BFA

1. Carry out NSP to make sure the Rifle is in the unloaded state.
2. Rotate the LOCKING NUT anti-clockwise to release it, using the COMBINATION TOOL.
3. Rotate the tube anti-clockwise until disengaged from the BODY.
4. Withdraw the TUBE from the BODY to its fullest extent.
5. Locate the BFA over FLASH ELIMINATOR, fit the TUBE into the ELIMINATOR engaging the CATCH on the BODY onto the rear end of the ELIMINATOR.
6. Hold BFA in position, insert the TUBE in BODY, rotate it clock-wise until secured to the flash eliminator. Do not overtighten.
7. Tighten the LOCKING NUT finger tight, use the COMBINATION TOOL to secure the LOCKING NUT.

To Remove the BFA.

1. Ensure the weapon is unloaded.
2. Reverse the procedure.

Skill at Arms & Shooting

Cleaning and Maintenance

As with all weapons the BFA must be cleaned and maintained.

1. When not in use, it is to be kept clean and lightly oiled.
2. Preparation for firing requires the attachment to be dry cleaned and checked that it fits correctly.
3. Cleaning after firing, requires all fouling visable, both inside and outside the attachment must be removed and then lightly oiled.

Operation

1. Using BLANK AMMUNITION a magazine is filled in the normal way.
2. The GAS PLUG is set to 'N' This should ensure that ejected cases travel approximately the same distance as BALL round.
3. Handling drills are as taught in rifle lessons.
4. Rapid rates of fire as for the Rifle/LSW are never to be exceeded.
5. Weapons are not to be tampered with or modified in any way.
6. Hearing protection will be worn by all personnel when firing BLANK ammunition or in close proximity to the firer.

Safety when firing Blank Ammunition

1. BLANK AMMUNITION will **only be fired with a BFA fitted.**
2. There is a 30 metres danger area to the front of any weapon firing blank. A Rifle firing BLANK is never to be pointed directly at anyone within 30 metres.
3. During any type of training where the participants may appear unexpectedly in close proximity to the firer, eg., CQB exercises in clearing buildings etc.
4. It is mandatory that EAR DEFENDERS will be worn by all firers, those supervising and others in the immediate area of those firing.
5. BLANK AMMUNITION ONLY will be used with the BFA.
6. The rounds of this AMMUNITION are of the same shape and length as ball ammunition. with a crimped end sealed with varnish.
7. It is your personal responsibility to recognise the difference between the different types of AMMUNITION.
8. GRENADE CARTRIDGES WILL NOT BE USED AS A SUBSTITUTE FOR BLANK.

9. Failure to set the correct gas setting can have dire consequences. The velocity of an ejected case rearwards at a higher rate than normal can inflect injuries to other firers and those in the vicinity. This may also cause damage to the Rifle.

Skill at Arms & Shooting

OPERATIONAL SAFETY

When circumstances dictate in an 'operational situation' the following SAFETY RULES must be followed:-

SAFE HANDLING WITH A MAGAZINE FITTED

1. Once an order has been given to"LOAD", you keep your weapon in that state until ordered to"UNLOAD". At all times you are responsible for the SAFE HANDLING of your Weapon.
2. The SAFETY CATCH is always at 'S' unless the situation demands otherwise, the FINGER is OFF the TRIGGER and the MUZZLE is pointed in a SAFE direction.
3. If a LOADED weapon is to be CARRIED IN A VEHICLE or on an AIRCRAFT it should be correctly slung or secured in the rack provided.
4. The weapon is UNLOADED on command OR when no longer able to ensure its SAFETY, such as when handing it over to, or leaving it under guard of another soldier.
5 .If a LOADED weapon MUST be handed over, the SAFETY CATCH will be applied, the recipient WILL BE TOLD OF THE STATE OF THE WEAPON, i.e., "LOADED" or "READY". The recipient WILL repeat back the STATE. If they are CORRECT, the weapon will be handed over - ensuring that the MUZZLE is kept pointing in a SAFE direction.
6. If it is necessary to pick up a weapon WITH a MAGAZINE FITTED - UNLOAD the weapon as taught.

RISK TO HEARING. Small Arms FULL BORE.

Ear Defenders or other suitable hearing protection must be worn by those firing and firing point staff during all full bore firing.

SA BLANK.

Hearing protection must be worn at all times for SA 80 BLANK firing PROVIDED that the following limits ARE applied:-

a. Blank Firing Attachment is ALWAYS fitted.

b. You are exposed to a LIMIT of up to 90 rounds per day.

c. That there are NO reflecting surfaces in the vicinity.

Those NOT firing are NOT to be closer than TEN metres to the flank of the weapon.

"BE SAFETY CONSCIOUS AT ALL TIMES "

CARRYING OUT SAFETY PRECAUTIONS.

As with all SKILL at ARMS training the first thing you must learn is the drill to carry out the NORMAL SAFETY PRECAUTIONS. (NSP). Safety Precautions will always be carried out at the beginning and end of every lesson, practice or range period, and immediately on returning from a patrol or exercise or duty, and when handing the weapon over to anyone.

To carry out the SAFETY PRECAUTIONS with a weapon adopt the LOW PORT POSITION as shown in the illustration on the left.

LOW PORT POSITION

On the command "FOR INSPECTION PORT ARMS"

1. Hold by PISTOL GRIP with the RIGHT hand, forefinger outside the TRIGGER GUARD. Point MUZZLE upwards and rest the butt on waist belt or right pouch. Tilt weapon to the right.

THIS IS THE POSITION ADOPTED TO CARRY OUT THE FULL ROUTINE OF SAFETY PRECAUTIONS.

2. Make sure that the SAFETY CATCH is at SAFE **(S)** and the CHANGE LEVER to Repetition **(R)**.
3. Cock the WEAPON. To do this, tilt it slightly to the RIGHT and, using the left hand over the top of the weapon, weapon, gripping the COCKING HANDLE with thumb and forefinger and pull FULLY to the rear.
4. Hold the COCKING HANDLE back with the forefinger - depress the HOLDING OPEN CATCH with the thumb, ease the COCKING HANDLE forward until the CATCH stops the forward movement of the CARRIER. When done, place LEFT hand underneath HAND GUARD.
5. For the weapon to be inspected, push it away from your body, horizontal to the ground and tilting to the left, so the breech can be inspected. After it has been inspected adopt the LOW PORT POSITION.
6. On the command **'EASE SPRINGS'**:-

(a) With the LEFT hand operate the BOLT RELEASE CATCH, letting the working part go forward.
(b) Put SAFETY CATCH to FIRE **(F)** with RIGHT forefinger.
(c) Operate the TRIGGER.
(d) Put the SAFETY CATCH to **(S)** using your LEFT thumb.
(e) Close the DUST COVER with RIGHT hand, folding up and back in its slot.

(f) Ground Arms ensuring that the weapon is laid on its left side - COCKING HANDLE uppermost.

(g) Undo pouches, remove MAGAZINES and contents for inspection. When the inspection has been completed, you put the MAGAZINES back in your POUCHES, FASTEN YOUR POUCHES, pick up your weapon and adopt LOW PORT position.

THESE SAFETY PRECAUTIONS MUST BE CARRIED OUT BY EVERYONE IN THE SQUAD TAKING PART IN THE TRAINING OR WHEN WEAPONS ARE BEING HANDLED - THIS INCLUDES ALL INSTRUCTORS AND ALL OTHER RANKS PRESENT.

BASIC MECHANISM OPERATION

The operation of the basic mechanism is the same for both the 5.56 Rifle and the LSW.

Mechanism - how the weapon works.

1. When the safety catch is at `**S**' the TRIGGER cannot be fully operated.
2. When the safety catch is at `**F**' and the TRIGGER is pressed, the HAMMER is released and hits the rear of the FIRING PIN, driving it forward on to the CAP in the BASE of the ROUND. The ROUND is fired and GASSES are produced which drive the BULLET up the BARREL.
3. Some of this GAS enters the GAS BLOCK and is diverted by the GAS PLUG into the GAS CYLINDER, pushing the PISTON to the rear and at the same time compressing the PISTON SPRING.
4. The rear of the PISTON strikes the CARRIER, forcing it backwards. The compressed PISTON SPRING re-asserts itself and forces the PISTON forwards again.
5. The BOLT is unlocked by the rearward movement of the CARRIER forcing the CAM STUD down the CAM STUD SLOT.
6. The CARRIER and BOLT go back together, cocking the HAMMER as they go. The EMPTY CASE is withdrawn from the CHAMBER by the EXTRACTOR and ejected out of the weapon to the right, through the EJECTION OPENING.

The RETURN SPRING on the GUIDE ROD is also compressed at this stage. Rearward movement of the CARRIER and BOLT ceases when the rear of the CARRIER strikes the BUFFER.

7. The RETURN SPRING re-asserts itself and aided by the BUFFER drives the CARRIER and BOLT. As it does so the BOLT feeds the next ROUND out of the MAGAZINE and into the CHAMBER. The EXTRACTOR grips the ROUND and the EJECTOR is compressed. The BOLT is rotated to lock into the BARREL EXTENSION by the continuing forward movement of the CARRIER, forcing the CAM STUD to slide up the CAM STUD SLOT. It is only when the parts are fully forward and locked that the SAFETY SEAR can operate to free the HAMMER into its ready position. A distinct CLICK will be heard.

8. The weapon is now ready to fire again. This action will continue each time the TRIGGER is operated until the last ROUND has been fired and the rearward action takes place. The working parts will then be held to the rear by the HOLDING OPEN CATCH being lifted up by the MAGAZINE PLATFORM.

BASIC MECHANISM

With the change lever at AUTOMATIC (**`A'**). The operation of the mechanism as previously explained applies equally to the AUTOMATIC role.

The difference being that the weapon will continue to fire as long as the TRIGGER is kept pressed and there are are ROUNDS left in the MAGAZINE.

The SAFETY SEAR allows one shot only per TRIGGER operation with the CHANGE LEVER at **`R'**.

When the CHANGE LEVER is at **`A'** the SAFETY SEAR is held out of its working position and AUTOMATIC fire results.

SIGHTS

The Weapon may be fitted with two types of day SIGHT, either the **Sight Unit Small Arms Trilux (SUSAT)** or an **IRON SIGHT.**

SUSAT SIGHT

The SUSAT consists of an OPTICAL BODY fixed to a MOUNTING BRACKET. On top of the SIGHT BODY is the EMERGENCY BATTLE SIGHT (EBS). Each sight has its own unique number, stamped on the underneath left side of the OPTICAL BODY. **You would be well advised to remember this number.**

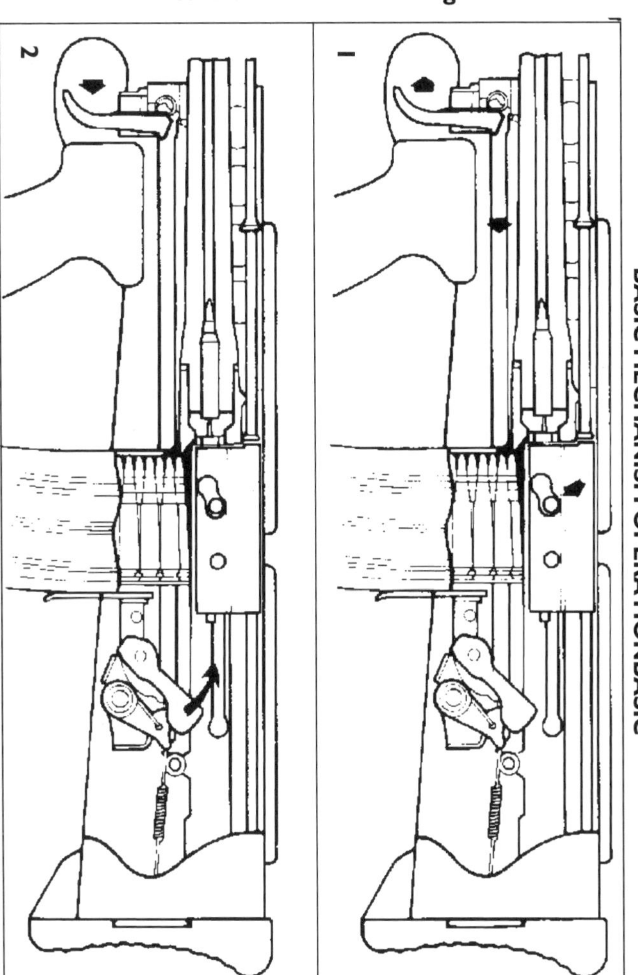

BASIC MECHANISM OPERATIONBASIC

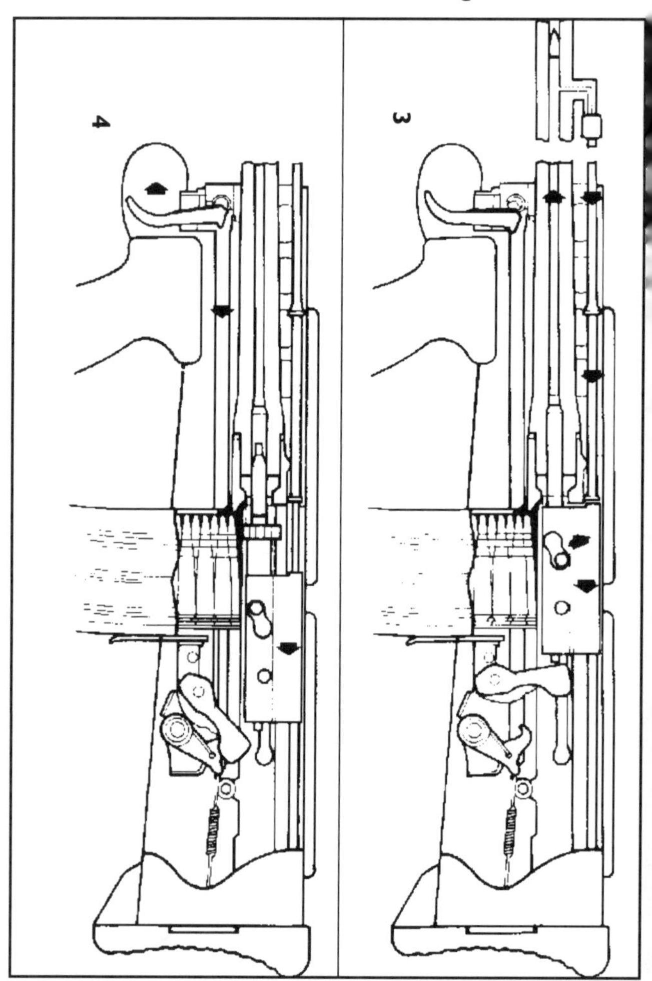
4
3

SIGHT SETTING

The SUSAT sight as illustrated below.
The RANGE DRUM is graduated in units of 100 from 300 to 800 metres.
Sights are set at a BATTLE RANGE of 300 metres, and should be used for normal infantry work. To set a RANGE, turn the DRUM until the required figure is facing straight to the rear.
The OPTICAL BODY contains the OPTICAL SYSTEM which has a magnification factor of x 4 and a field of view of 177 mils.

The BODY comprises :-

The EYEPIECE which is made of rubber and is glued to the rear of the optics. It is designed to protect the LENS from water and of a length to ensure correct positioning of the eye.
The POINTER within the OPTICS is seen in your field of view. In daylight the POINTER appears as a dark pillar with a clear centre. At night POINTER tip can be illuminated by the TRILUX lamp. The light from the lamp is reflected up into the pointer and is seen as a reddish glow.
A BRIGHTNESS CONTROL is located at the RIGHT REAR of the BODY and can be rotated to change the light intensity from zero to full brightness.
The OBJECTIVE LENS HOOD is part of the BODY which is shaped to overhang the OBJECTIVE LENS, so reducing reflections and also protecting the LENS from rain.

EMERGENCY BATTLE SIGHT (EBS)

The EBS consists of a BLADE FORESIGHT and an APERTURE BACKSIGHT. It is matched to the OPTICAL CENTRE of the SUSAT lenses during manufacture and therefore no zeroing adjustment is provided. It is for use in an emergency should the SUSAT become damaged, until such time that the IRON SIGHT can be fitted in its place.

SIGHT MOUNTING BRACKET consists of:-

The MOUNTING SHOE and SIGHT MOUNT. The MOUNTING SHOE is dovetailed to match the SIGHT BASE on the weapon.
A LOCATING PLUNGER protrudes through the SHOE to engage in one of the three holes in the SIGHT BASE.
Two CLAMPING UNITS secure the SHOE to the SIGHT BASE.
A lifting plate for the PLUNGER protrudes on the RIGHT side of the BRACKET. This enables the fore/aft position of the SIGHT to be adjusted to give you the most comfortable SIGHT PICTURE, you can then mark the position for your own use.
The SIGHT MOUNT links the MOUNTING SHOE with the OPTICAL BODY.

For zeroing purposes, the MOUNT is fitted at the FRONT with a HORIZONTAL adjustment screw, at the REAR is a VERTICAL adjustment screw and immediately below the EYE PIECE is a RANGE DRUM which is marked from 3 to 8 in increments of 100 metres.

FITTING THE SUSAT

1. Check sight serial number is correct one for your particular weapon.
2. Rotate RANGE DRUM so that the 300 metre setting is faces directly to the rear. Release the SIGHT CLAMPING NUTS and open the weapon TOP COVER.
3. Hold the weapon with the RIGHT hand and grip SUSAT with the LEFT hand.

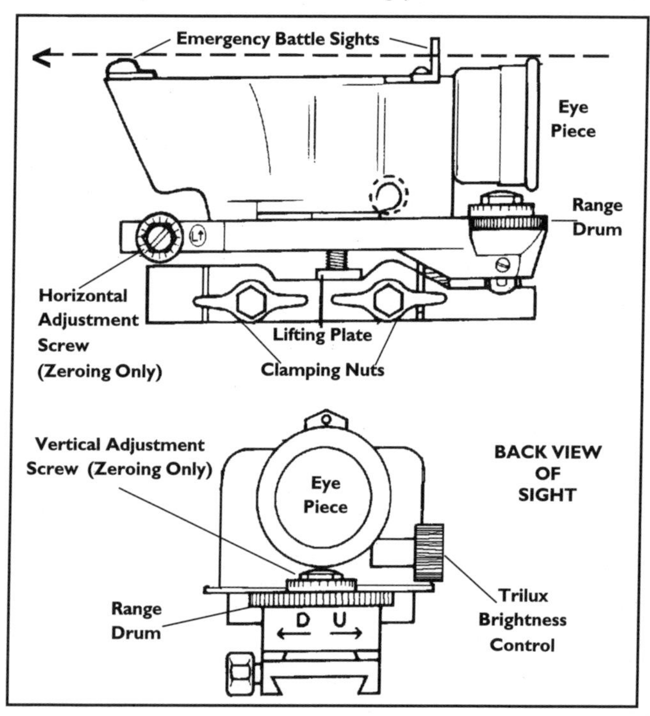

4. Using your forefinger to raise the LIFTING PLATE and withdraw LOCATING PLUNGER, align the rear of the MOUNTING SHOE with the front of the SIGHT BASE, then slide the SIGHT towards the rear of the weapon until the required position is reached, then release the LIFTING PLATE.
5. Check that LOCATING PLUNGER has engaged in correct recess on SIGHT BASE. Test by attempting to move the SIGHT forwards or backwards. Tighten CLAMPING NUTS - DO NOT OVER TIGHTEN. Close the weapon TOP COVER.
6. FOR SIGHT ADJUSTMENTS, see SETTING & ADJUSTMENTS.

REMOVING THE SUSAT

1. Note exact position of LIFTING PLATE in relation to SIGHT BASE. (To accurately refit the SIGHT).
2. Hold the weapon by the PISTOL GRIP with the right hand so that it is horizontal and upright.

Open TOP COVER and undo the SIGHT CLAMPING NUTS.

3. Grip the SUSAT with the left hand, use the forefinger to raise the LIFTING PLATE and disengage the LOCATING LUG from the SIGHT BASE, then slide SUSAT forward and off the SIGHT BASE. Close the TOP COVER of the weapon.
4. Check and make a note of the SERIAL NUMBER of the SUSAT.

The IRON SIGHT

The IRON SIGHT consists of a FORESIGHT BLOCK and a CARRYING HANDLE, which incorporates a dual leaf APERTURE BACKSIGHT.
THE FORESIGHT consists of a BLADE mounted in a FORESIGHT BLOCK, the base of which contains a female dovetail which fits into its matching male dovetail on top of the weapon GAS BLOCK.
The two are held together by a RETAINING SCREW. The FORESIGHT BLADE is protected by extensions of the BLOCK and the rear of the BLADE houses a TRILUX element which emits light through a small hole. 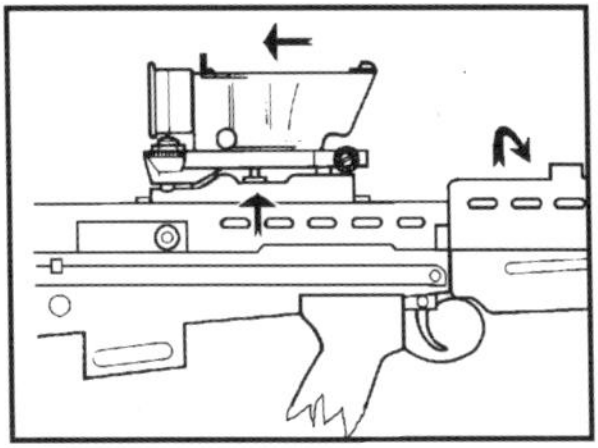
A vertical adjustment screw, retained by a LOCKING PLUNGER, provides for ZEROING adjustment.

Fitting the IRON SIGHT

1. Loosen the FORESIGHT RETAINING SCREW fully, using the COMBINATION TOOL.
2. Ensure the TRILUX element is facing to the rear, mate the dovetail joints, check that the sight is flush front and rear then tighten the RETAINING SCREW - DO NOT OVER TIGHTEN.
3. Using the COMBINATION TOOL, loosen the CARRYING HANDLE RETAINING SCREWS and release the LOCATING SCREW sufficiently for the handle to slide easily along the SIGHT BASE dovetail.
4. Open the weapon TOP COVER and slide the HANDLE rear-wards on to the SIGHT BASE to the required position, ensuring the LOCATING SCREW aligns with one of the three holes in the SIGHT BASE. Tighten the LOCATING SCREW and RETAINING SCREWS - DO NOT OVER TIGHTEN. Close the weapon TOP COVER.

NOTE: When an IRON SIGHT has been fitted as a replacement for the SUSAT sight, then the weapon must be zeroed - Refer to SETTING and ADJUSTMENTS.

Removing the IRON SIGHT

1. Fully release the FORESIGHT BLOCK RETAINING SCREW and slide the BLOCK off the dovetail. Tighten the RETAINING SCREW.
2. Open the weapon TOP COVER, loosen the RETAINING SCREWS and the LOCATING SCREW on the CARRYING HANDLE, then slide the HANDLE forwards clear of the SIGHT BASE.
   Close the weapon TOP COVER.

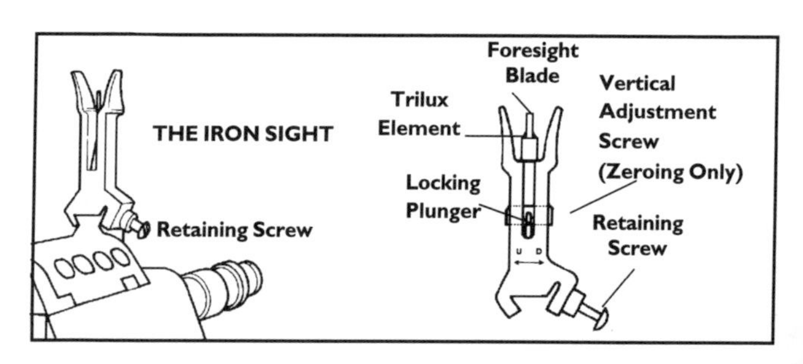

THE IRON SIGHT Backsight and Carrying Handle

The BACKSIGHT and CARRYING HANDLE is fitted to the SIGHT BASE by means of matching dovetails.
The handle is positioned by a LOCATING SCREW which engages in one of three holes in the SIGHT BASE, and is secured by two RETAINING SCREWS.
The BACKSIGHT has two LEAF APERTURES, a small one for ranges up to 200m and a larger one for use - in conjunction with the TRILUX element -in conditions of low light or darkness. To change the APERTURE, push the LEAF forwards or backwards. Extensions on the HANDLE protect the apertures.
A horizontal adjusting screw on the right side, retained by a locking plunger, is used for zeroing.

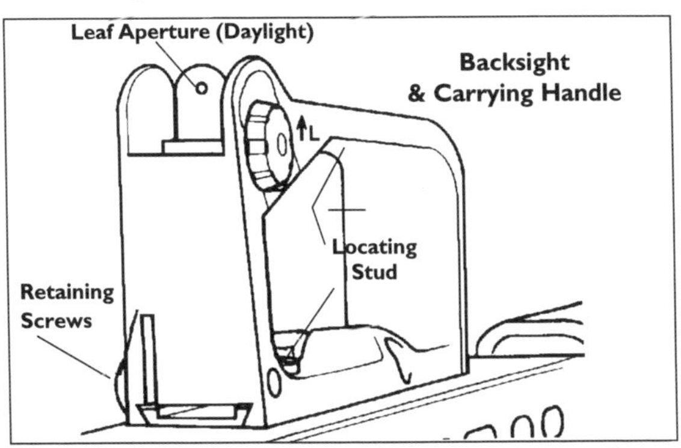

SUSAT SIGHT WARNING

CONTAINS A GASEOUS TRITIUM LIGHT SOURCE (GTLS), DO NOT ADJUST OR STRIP THE **SIGHT.** ACTION ON DISCOVERY OF A DAMAGED GTLS ARE AS FOLLOWS:-

1. DO NOT TOUCH THE GTLS.
2. DO NOT INHALE THE ESCAPING GAS.
3. VENTILATE AND EVACUATE THE AREA.
4. INFORM RADIATION PROTECTION SUPERVISOR.
5. WASH HANDS THOROUGHLY, DO **NOT** USE SOAP

Skill at Arms & Shooting

SELF CHECK TEST QUESTIONS

1. Give the nine rules for safely handling weapons.
2. Name the three types of 5.56 rounds.
3. What distinguishes the types of round.
4. What are the firing modes.
5. What are the locking features of the weapons.
6. Give the muzzle velocity of the 5.56 Rifle and LSW.
7. Explain Recoil (joules)
8. Which direction does the rifling turn in the Barrel.
9. What does SUSAT stand for.
10. What is the Field of View with the Optical Sight.
11. What are the Range Settings of the Optical sight
12. With the Iron Sight Back Sight how many apertures does it have.
13. What Range setting is the Iron Sight
14. Give the weight of the LSW with SUSAT sight and full Magazine.
15. What is the difference betwen the 5.56 Rifle and the LSW.
16. What is done before and after a WT lesson.
17. How many straps make up the Rifle Sling
18. What is the saw blade meant to be used for.
19. If required to pick up a weapon with mag fited, what action do you take.
20. What position is adopted to carry out the NSP's.
21. Give the procedure (five points) to carry out NSP's.
22. On command "ease springs" give the seven procedures/actions taken.
23. Why align the Ejector on the Bolt with the Cam Stud Recess in the Carrier"
24. How many Cleaning Rods are needed to clean a full length barrel.
25. How do you remove carbon fouling.
26. When examining the Barrel which end do you look through.
27. Cleaning in Adverse Conditions, what is issued to help care and cleaning.
28. Name the three types of Ammunition used and how are they identified.
29. Functional Failures (IA's) What is the first important rule to be observed.
30. What is done with a Round involved in a stoppage.
31. What action do you take if you have a Separated Case.

FILLING A MAGAZINE - USING THE CHARGER

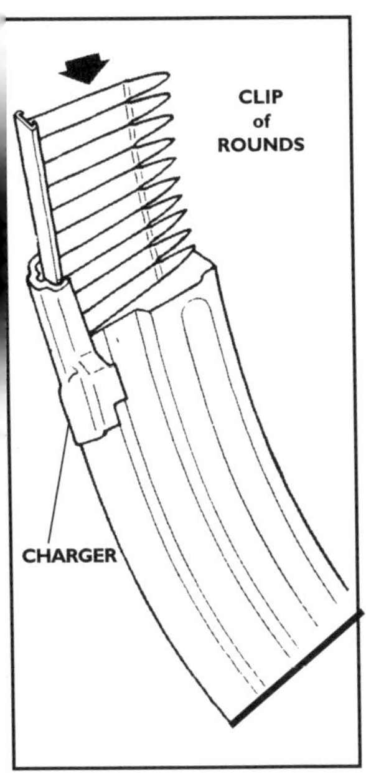

1. Having inspected the MAGAZINE, grip it in LEFT hand, support on a firm surface, ensure the back of MAGAZINE is facing away from the BODY.

2. Fit the wide end of CHARGER onto the back of MAGAZINE, ensure that it is fully seated.

3. Put CLIP of 10 ROUNDS into the Charger.

4. Using your RIGHT thumb, push down on the top ROUND, until all ROUNDS are fed into MAGAZINE. Remove the CLIP.

5. Each time clip is fed into MAGAZINE ensure that BASE of last ROUND is firm against the rear wall of the MAGAZINE. When the MAGAZINE is full remove the CHARGER and retain in pouch for further use.

FILLING WITH LOOSE ROUNDS

1. Hold MAGAZINE as when using CHARGER.
2. Push ROUNDS into MAGAZINE, depressing the PLATFORM, BULLETS towards the narrow wall of the MAGAZINE, one at a time, making sure that the BASE of each ROUND is firm against the MAGAZINE REAR WALL.

EMPTYING MAGAZINES

SHOULD YOU DROP A ROUND - MAKE SURE IT IS CLEAN BEFORE USING IT TO FILL YOUR MAGAZINE

Using an empty CLIP, press down on each SECOND ROUND, to allow the TOP ROUND to drop out. Ensure ROUNDS do not drop into dirt/ mud.

A second method is to hold the MAGAZINE in the LEFT HAND, BULLETS pointing away from body, then push the BASE of the ROUND forward so that it disengages from the GUIDE LIPS. Care must be taken as you may have to twist and pull the ROUND clear with your free hand.

This is a useful method, especially at night as it makes very little noise.

LOAD, READY and UNLOAD

The weapon is LOADED when it has a MAGAZINE inserted. It is READY to FIRE when the weapon is COCKED and a LIVE ROUND is in the CHAMBER. It is UNLOADED when the MAGAZINE has been removed and there is no ROUND in the CHAMBER.

On the command "LOAD":

1. You adopt the 'LOW PORT' position.
2. Set SAFETY CATCH at **'S'** (safe).
3. Tilt weapon to RIGHT, take a full MAGAZINE or one with number of ROUNDS ordered, check top ROUNDS are in position correctly, insert it FIRMLY into MAGAZINE HOUSING.
   Ensure the MAGAZINE is clicked fully home and is secure.
4. Fasten your POUCH.

On the command "READY": with the weapon loaded:-

1. Adopt the 'ALERT' position - that is :- Advance the LEFT foot, bring the BUTT into the shoulder, point the MUZZLE down.
2. Check CHANGE LEVER is at **'R'**.
3. Set SIGHTS at 300 or as ordered. Pull the COCKING HANDLE fully to the rear, then release it cleanly to go forward, assist.
4. Set the SAFETY CATCH to **'F'**, place your finger on the TRIGGER and observe.

Skill at Arms & Shooting

NOTE: You may be ordered to return the SAFETY CATCH to `**S**', if so, put your forefinger along outside of TRIGGER GUARD.

On the command "UNLOAD":-

1. Re-position your finger outside the TRIGGER GUARD.
2. Put the SAFETY CATCH to `**S**'.
3. Unfasten the POUCH. Adopt the LOW PORT position, tilt the weapon to the RIGHT. Grip the MAGAZINE with the LEFT hand, press the MAGAZINE CATCH with your thumb and remove the MAGAZINE and put it in your POUCH.

NOTE: THE MAGAZINE MUST BE REMOVED AT THIS STAGE FOR SAFETY REASONS.

5. Keeping the weapon pointing in a SAFE direction COCK the weapon carefully, to prevent the ROUND ejecting too far, and engage the HOLDING OPEN CATCH. Tilt the weapon to the LEFT and visually check that the BODY and CHAMBER are clear, then operate the BOLT RELEASE to allow the WORKING PARTS to go forward. At night check the BODY and CHAMBER are clear by inserting your finger.

NOTE: Should you have gloves on or have any difficulty in feeling that the CHAMBER is clear, put the weight of your PULLTHROUGH into the CHAMBER, if it drops into the BARREL -the CHAMBER IS CLEAR.

6. Put SAFETY CATCH to `**F**', operate the TRIGGER, then return the SAFETY CATCH to `**S**', put SIGHTS down to 300 if necessary.
7. Close DUST COVER, pick up EJECTED ROUND, clean and replace in MAGAZINE, fasten POUCH.

USEFUL TIPS:-To prevent possible injury to the face or eye from EJECTED ROUNDS - DON'T TILT WEAPON TO LEFT WHEN COCKING DURING UNLOAD.

Keep your weapon pointing in SAFE direction, RIGHT HAND should be cupped over EJECTION OPENING to prevent ejected ROUND from being lost especially in the dark.

MAKING SAFE

When ordered to "MAKE SAFE", no matter what 'state of readiness' the weapon is in, UNLOAD as you have been taught, then put on a FULL MAGAZINE

SAFE HANDLING WITH THE MAGAZINE FITTED.

Once an order has been given to "LOAD", you keep the weapon in that state until ordered to "UNLOAD".

"SAFETY IS A PERSONAL RESPONSIBILITY"

FUNCTIONAL FAILURES - IMMEDIATE ACTION

If the weapon fails to fire, or stops firing carry out the IMMEDIATE ACTION (IA) drills. It is only with practice that these become second nature to you. The IA drills are described below:- The most important rule is to - ALWAYS LOOK AT THE POSITION OF THE COCKING HANDLE.

1. If the COCKING HANDLE is fully to the REAR, and MAGAZINE is EMPTY - change MAGAZINE - operate BOLT RELEASE - aim - test and adjust - continue firing.
2. If the COCKING HANDLE is NOT fully to the REAR - cock the weapon - engage the HOLDING OPEN CATCH - look into BODY and CHAMBER:-
   a. If CHAMBER empty and there are ROUNDS in MAGAZINE - check MAGAZINE fitted correctly - operate BOLT RELEASE - re-aim - test and adjust - continue firing.
   b. If LIVE ROUND or EMPTY CASE is in BODY or CHAMBER - remove MAGAZINE - clear obstruction - replace MAGAZINE - operate BOLT RELEASE - re-aim - test and adjust - continue firing.
3. It is important that ANY ROUND which has been involved in a stoppage or used as a tool, whether it appears damaged or not, is **NOT** to be loaded into a MAGAZINE or any attempt made to fire it.

GAS STOPPAGE.

If after carrying out the IA the weapon fires one or two rounds and then stops again, and after repeating the IA the same condition arises:-

1. Operate the BOLT RELEASE, put SAFETY CATCH to **'S'** and using a ROUND or the COMBINATION TOOL - turn the GAS PLUG so that the PLUNGER engages the 'E' EXCESS GAS SETTING.
2. Put SAFETY CATCH to **'F'** - aim - test and adjust - continue firing.
3. As soon as is practicable the GAS ASSEMBLY must be cleaned and reset to the 'N' (NORMAL) setting.

FURTHER ACTION

If an obstruction in the CHAMBER cannot be removed during the IA, or obstructions occur repeatedly, or the weapon will not fire after carrying out the IA, then:-

1. UNLOAD the weapon - remove TMH - BOLT - BOLT CARRIER .
2. Inspect and check EXTRACTOR - EJECTOR - RETAINING PINS - FIRING PIN PROTRUSION and the CHAMBER.
3. If BOLT parts are damaged or loose, fit serviceable SPARE BOLT ASSEMBLY.
4. If the obstructed CHAMBER is due to a broken/damaged EXTRACTOR:- Replace the BOLT with the spare assembly, cock the weapon to allow the EXTRACTOR to grip the base of a ROUND and remove the obstruction, engage the HOLDING OPEN CATCH and visually inspect the CHAMBER through the EJECTION OPENING.

If the CHAMBER is clear, reload and operate the BOLT RELEASE, set the CHANGE LEVER as required, put the SAFETY CATCH to `**F**', test and adjust, and continue to fire.

If the CHAMBER does not appear to be obstructed and there are no damaged parts, examine the CHAMBER and if there is a SEPARATED CASE - refer your weapon to the armourer.

If continued stoppages occur, the weapon should be thoroughly cleaned and examined. Particular attention must be paid to the parts of the GAS SYSTEM.

These should be cleaned and gauged, using the COMBINATION TOOL SCRAPERS, after every 200 ROUNDS fired, regardless of satisfactory functioning of the system.

STRIPPING & ASSEMBLING - as illustrated on page 5.

The sequence of stripping the weapon is important to prevent damage to the working parts. It will NOT be stripped further than taught. The weapon is stripped into the following groups/assemblies:-

MAGAZINE. SIGHTS. TRIGGER MECHANISM HOUSING (TMH) BARREL. BREECH ASSEMBLY. GAS SYSTEM. BOLT CARRIER ASSEMBLY. RECOIL ROD ASSEMBLY.

THE WEAPON STRIPPED

General Information.

In order to maintain your weapon in a satisfactory working condition, periodic stripping and cleaning is necessary. In addition to ensuring that the component parts are clean and lubricated, any undue wear can be detected and the relevant part replaced as necessary.
The only tools to be used are those provided in the Tool Roll. In your early stages of training NO time limits are imposed during practising Stripping and Assembling.
As the weapon is stripped the parts must be laid out on a clean and dry surface, it follows that it must be clean when assembled.
Stripping other than that you have been instructed to do will NOT be carried out.
The regular care and cleaning of will ensure that it is in a serviceable condition at all times.
Your ability to look after a weapon will be reflected in the high standard of Weapon Training required to pass your Training Tests.
Regular stripping and assembling does cause "wear and tear" on any weapon.
This is especially important with the SUSAT, stripping and assembling should not be carried out without due reason.
Any defects noticed must be reported immediately to the unit Armourer.

STRIPPING and ASSEMBLING

1. Check SAFETY CATCH is at `**S**' and the CHANGE LEVER is at `**R**'.

2. Cock weapon, engage HOLDING OPEN CATCH, inspect BODY and CHAMBER and face of the bolt to ensure they are all clear.

Operate BOLT RELEASE to allow WORKING PARTS to go forward. DO NOT operate the TRIGGER. DO NOT close DUST COVER.

3. The SAFETY CATCH must remain on `**S**' and the HAMMER must remain cocked throughout the time the weapon is in a stripped state.

4. The SUSAT and or the IRON SIGHT should not be removed unless it is impossible to clean the weapon correctly without doing so.

TRIGGER MECHANISM HOUSING (TMH)

See illustration on the next page.

To STRIP:-

1. Ensure the weapon is horizontal and upside down. Fully withdraw the TMH (TRIGGER MECHANISM HOUSING) rear LOCKING PIN, then re-insert the pin approximately 5mm into the BODY, so that the GROOVE nearest the BODY is flush with the outside of its housing - a distinct click should be heard. This ensures that the end of the PIN retains the RECOIL ROD ASSEMBLY while the TMH is being removed.
2. Finally withdraw the TMH FORWARD LOCKING PIN and separate the TMH from the BODY by pulling the BUTT upwards and disengaging the TMH from its FRONT CATCH.

To ASSEMBLE:-

1. Check that the TMH FRONT LOCKING PIN is fully withdrawn. Insert front end of TMH into CATCH behind HAND GUARD.

Raise back of TMH and press the BODY and TMH together. Fully insert the TMH REAR LOCKING PIN, then the front LOCKING PIN.

2. Test the action by COCKING the weapon and engaging the HOLDING OPEN CATCH, then operate, the BOLT RELEASE, set the SAFETY CATCH at `**R**' and operate the TRIGGER.
3. Put the SAFETY CATCH to `**S**' and close the DUST COVER.

NOTE: When/if applicable refit the SUSAT, ensuring that the LOCATING PLUNGER engages the correct recess in the SIGHT BASE to maintain correct EYE RELIEF.

RECOIL ROD and BOLT CARRIER ASSEMBLIES - see illustration on page 34.

To STRIP:-

1. Remove the TMH as detailed, keeping the weapon horizontal and upside down
2. Place a hand over the rear of the RECOIL ROD ASSEMBLY.

Fully withdraw the TMH LOCKING PIN, then under control, remove the RECOIL ROD ASSEMBLY. Do NOT separate the SPRING from the RECOIL ROD ASSEMBLY.

3. Pull the COCKING HANDLE to the rear to unlock the BOLT, then withdraw the HANDLE from the CARRIER.
4. Place hand over the rear of the BODY, raise the MUZZLE and slide out the BOLT CARRIER ASSEMBLY.

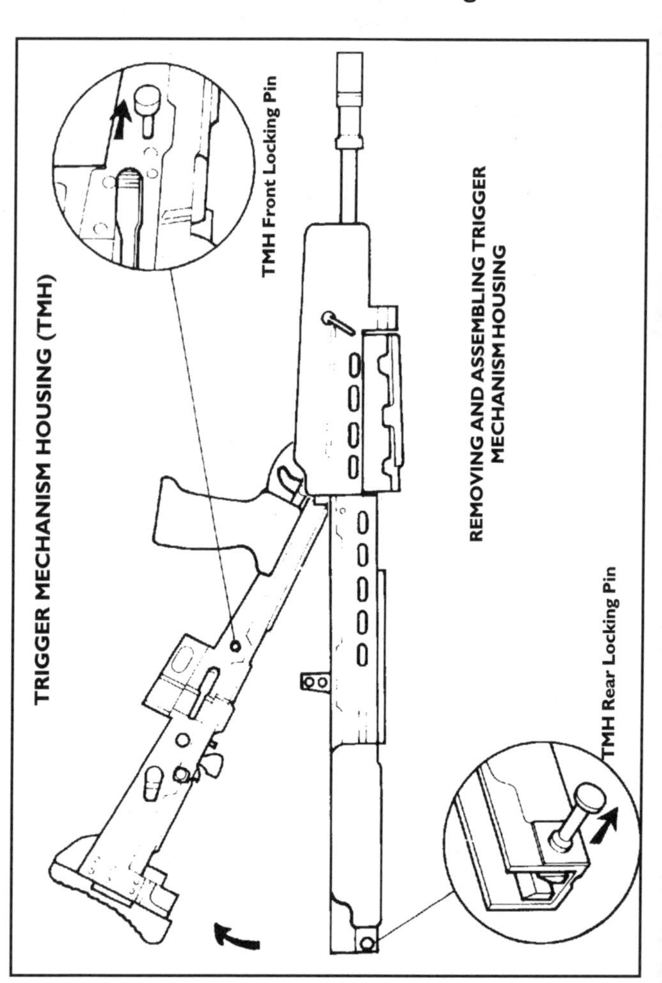
TRIGGER MECHANISM HOUSING (TMH)
TMH Front Locking Pin
REMOVING AND ASSEMBLING TRIGGER MECHANISM HOUSING
TMH Rear Locking Pin

5. Hold BOLT CARRIER ASSEMBLY in hand, withdraw FIRING PIN RETAINING PIN - use COMBINATION TOOL if necessary and withdraw the FIRING PIN from the rear of the BOLT.
6. Pull BOLT fully forward in the CARRIER and remove the CAM STUD. Separate the BOLT from the CARRIER.

ASSEMBLING RECOIL ROD & BOLT CARRIER ASSEMBLIES.

TO ASSEMBLE

1. Align the EJECTOR on the BOLT with the CAM STUD recess in the CARRIER.
2. Insert the BOLT into CARRIER, align the CAM STUD HOLE in the BOLT with the front of the CAM RECESS in the CARRIER.
3. Hold the CAM STUD so that the FIRING PIN HOLE in the STUD is aligned to allow the FIRING PIN to pass through it. Push the CAM STUD through the recess in the CARRIER and into position in the BOLT.
4. Insert the FIRING PIN through the back of the CARRIER and ensure that it is fully seated. Replace the FIRING PIN RETAINING PIN from the left side of the BOLT CARRIER.

When correctly seated the RETAINING PIN is flush with the sides of the CARRIER.

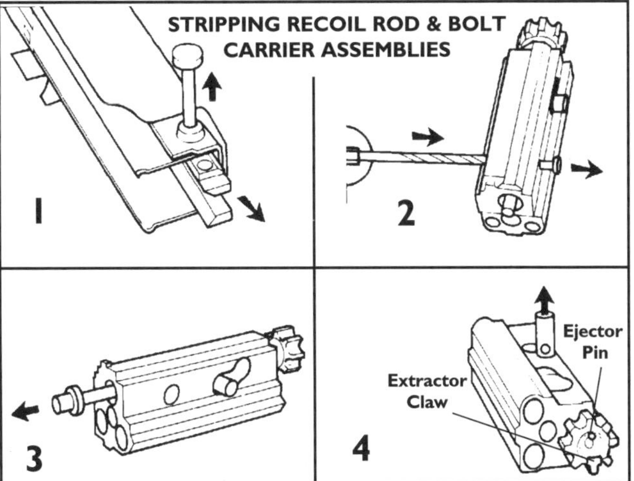

5. With the weapon horizontal and upside down, first ensure that the BOLT is fully forward in the CARRIER. Then place the CARRIER into the weapon and push far enough forward to align the COCKING HANDLE RECESS adjacent to the COCKING GUIDE in the BODY.

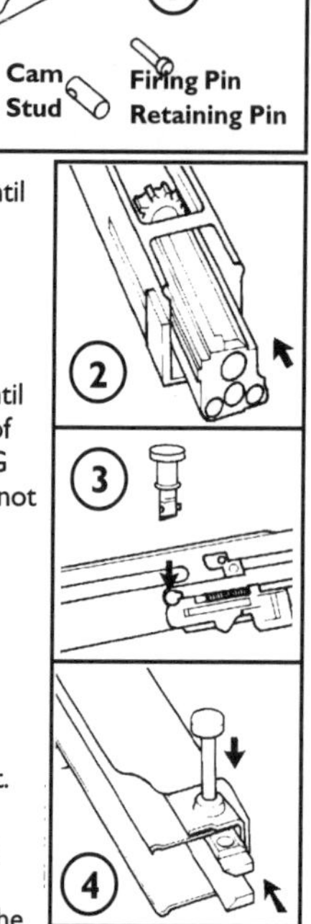

6. Insert the COCKING HANDLE through the side of the BODY and into the RECESS in the CARRIER. Push the CARRIER fully forward until the LOCKING SPINES on the BOLT have entered and locked into the BARREL EXTENSION.

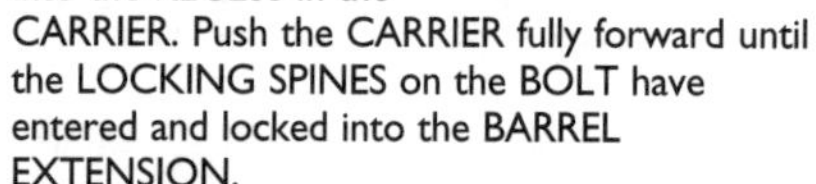

7. Align the RECOIL RODS and SPRING with the holes in the rear of the CARRIER. Push the RECOIL ROD ASSEMBLY into the weapon until the end of the ASSEMBLY is flush to the end of the BODY. Push in the TMH REAR LOCKING PIN to engage the end of the ASSEMBLY, but not sufficient to obstruct the centre area which accommodates the LUG of the TMH.

STRIPPING AND ASSEMBLING THE GAS SYSTEM

See illustrations on nxt page.

TO STRIP:-

1. Ensure that the weapon is horizontal but upright. Open the GAS ASSEMBLY TOP COVER.
2. Grip the GAS CYLINDER with the left hand and with the right hand push the PISTON to the rear against the action of its RETURN SPRING. Move the PISTON out of alignment with the CYLINDER, release the pressure and withdraw the PISTON, complete with SPRING, from the weapon. Do not separate the SPRING from the PISTON.
3. Remove the GAS CYLINDER from the GAS PLUG by pulling it to the rear. Make a note of the GAS SETTINGS positions on the GAS PLUG.

STRIP & ASSEMBLE THE GAS SYSTEM

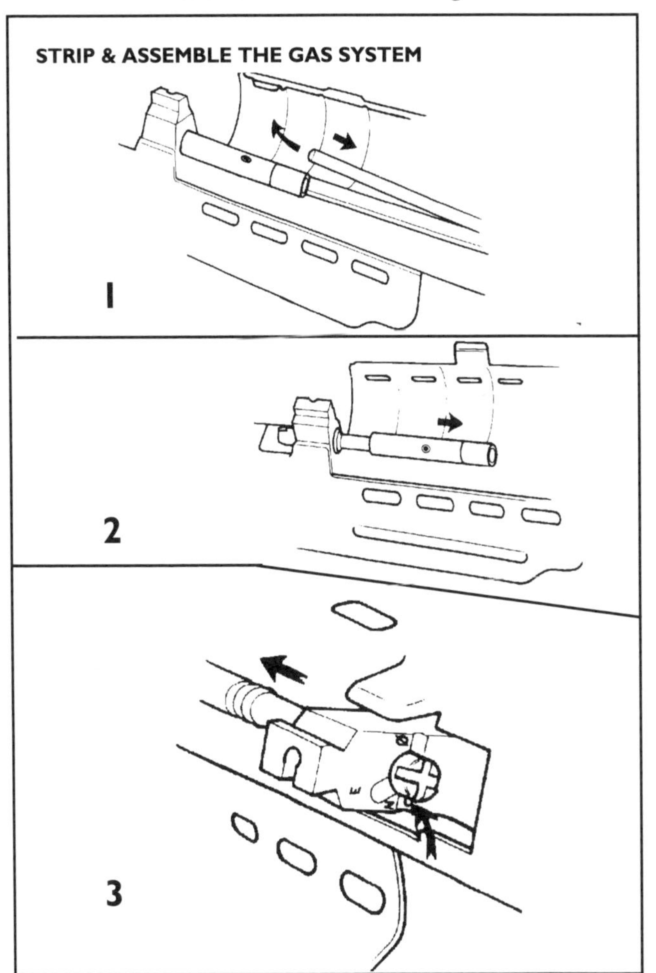

4. Remove the GAS PLUG by pressing the PLUNGER on the front of the PLUG and at the same time withdraw the PLUG from the rear of the GAS BLOCK, removing it from the weapon.

TO ASSEMBLE.

1. Insert the GAS PLUG into the rear of the GAS BLOCK. Depress the PLUNGER and at the same time push the PLUG through the BLOCK. Rotate the PLUG until the PLUNGER is aligned with the recess marked `N' (Normal) on the front of the GAS BLOCK.
2. Fit the CYLINDER onto the rear of the GAS PLUG and hold it in position with the left hand.
3. Turn the weapon on its side and carefully feed the SPRING END of the PISTON back into the CENTRAL HOLE above the BARREL EXTENSION. Push the PISTON to the rear to compress the SPRING, then align and engage the PISTON with the CYLINDER REAR RECESS. Close the TOP COVER.

NOTE: Should you have difficulty in locating the CENTRAL HOLE you can see through the VENTILATION SLITS in the BODY.

OPERATIONAL STRIPPING.

During tactical training or on operations, it may be undesirable to strip the complete weapon at any one time, in order to carry out maintenance. Accordingly, it is possible to strip only one part at a time, provided that the basic SAFETY PRECAUTIONS are taken. The GAS ASSEMBLY may be stripped provided the weapon is unloaded and the BOLT CARRIER ASSEMBLY is held to the rear. The TMH may be removed without removing any other part. As with normal stripping all parts should be placed, in the sequence of stripping, on a clean surface.

STRIPPING & ASSEMBLING MAGAZINE

To STRIP

1. Hold the MAGAZINE in the LEFT hand with the BOTTOM PLATE uppermost.

2. Push in the RETAINING STUD and slide off the BOTTOM PLATE in the direction of the forward edge. Remove the SPRING and PLATFORM from the MAGAZINE.

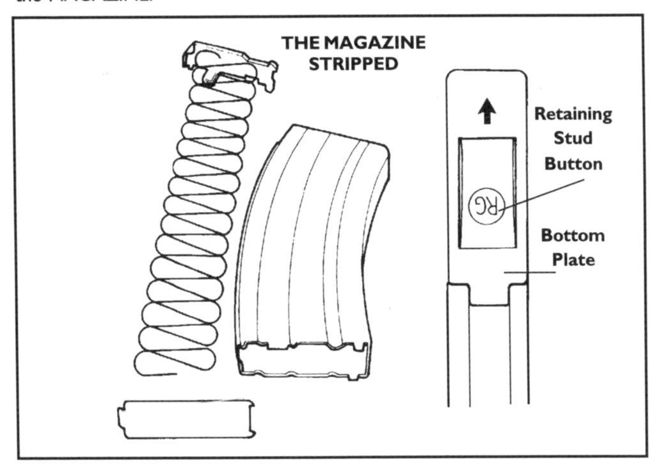

To ASSEMBLE

1. Ensure that the PLATFORM is aligned correctly, then insert the PLATFORM and SPRING into the MAGAZINE.

2. Push down the RETAINING STUD and slide on the BOTTOM PLATE. Ensure that the STUD engages in its recess in the BOTTOM PLATE.

Your weapon can be stripped in any sequence providing the NORMAL SAFETY PRECAUTIONS are first carried out.

Stripping is only carried out for a purpose, i.e., CLEANING and MAINTENANCE.

"Never strip a magazine further than you have been taught"

Skill at Arms & Shooting

USE OF CLEANING EQUIPMENT illustration next page.

THE TOOL ROLL is provided to carry all the items required for the cleaning of the weapon. The illustration sets out the items to be found in the TOOL ROLL which are described in the following paragraphs.

The **CLEANING ROD** - the 3 section Rod used with either the BORE or CHAMBER BRUSHES. (Two sets of RODS needed to clean a full BARREL length). Do not use if the screwed section joints are not close and smooth. Insert into MUZZLE end of Barrel, twist only clockwise, taking care not to rub it against the side of the bore at the MUZZLE.

The **BORE CLEANING BRUSH** is only to be used to clean the BORE of the WEAPON, oil may be applied to assist in removing fouling and stains within the BORE. It can also be used with the PULLTHROUGH, in which case only to be drawn from the CHAMBER end of the BARREL.

The **CHAMBER/BARREL EXTENSION BRUSH** is ONLY to be used for cleaning the CHAMBER, the BARREL EXTENSION or the interior of the GAS BLOCK. It is to be used ONLY with the CLEANING ROD. The **PULLTHROUGH** can be used instead of the ROD to draw a FLANNELETTE PATCH or the BORE BRUSH through the BARREL, it must first be unravelled and stretched to remove any knots or kinks.

A **FLANNELETTE PATCH** can be fitted folding it in half lengthways and putting it into the eyelet with equal parts of the flannelette protruding either side.

FLANNELETTE PATCHES are mainly used to dry clean and lubricate the barrel. They must not be used in a size larger than 50mm x 50mm or they will jam in the barrel.

NYLON PAD (SCOTCHBRIGHT). Used primarily for removing carbon fouling, but can also be used with oil to remove rust.

Must not be used on weapon parts coated with a protective finish as the pad will remove the finish.

The **NYLON BRUSH** is used with FLANNELETTE to clean the inside of the BODY. A piece of lightly oiled FLANNELETTE is used to clean the outside of the weapon.

COMBINATION TOOL. A multipurpose tool used when cleaning the weapon, fitting and adjusting SIGHTS, and adjusting GAS SYSTEM.

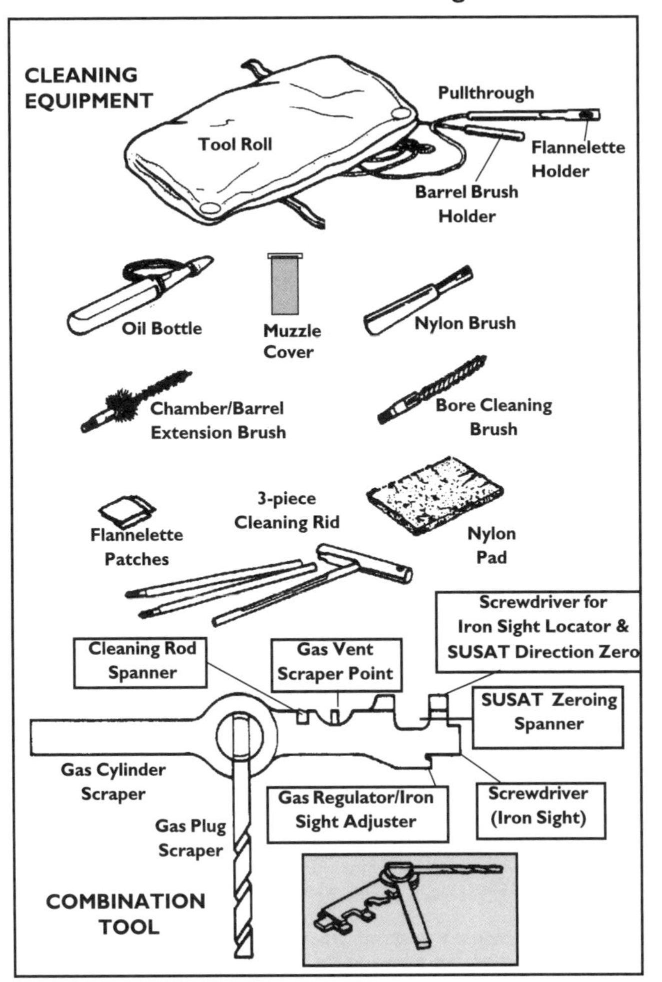

CLEANING EQUIPMENT
Tool Roll
Pullthrough
Flannelette Holder
Barrel Brush Holder
Oil Bottle
Muzzle Cover
Nylon Brush
Chamber/Barrel Extension Brush
Bore Cleaning Brush
Flannelette Patches
3-piece Cleaning Rid
Nylon Pad
Screwdriver for Iron Sight Locator & SUSAT Direction Zero
Cleaning Rod Spanner
Gas Vent Scraper Point
SUSAT Zeroing Spanner
Gas Cylinder Scraper
Gas Regulator/Iron Sight Adjuster
Screwdriver (Iron Sight)
Gas Plug Scraper
COMBINATION TOOL

CLEANING THE WEAPON.

FIRST CARRY OUT THE NSP's (Normal Safety Precautions)

1. Using the NYLON BRUSH remove any loose fouling or debris from the weapon parts. (Less the SUSAT)
2. Using a piece of lightly oiled FLANNELETTE, clean the outside of the weapon.
3. Using the CHAMBER/BARREL EXTENSION BRUSH and CLEANING ROD, insert it into the CHAMBER. With a clockwise rotating action, withdrawing the BRUSH with the MUZZLE pointing up will dislodge fouling or debris which will come out with BRUSH.
4. Using the NYLON BRUSH and FLANNELETTE, clean the inside of the body.
5. Clean the BARREL with the BORE BRUSH, then use the PULLTHROUGH and dry clean FLANNELETTE.
6. Examine the barrel for cleanliness. Look through the MUZZLE end by holding it up to the light about 150mm away from your head, keep both eyes open and follow the lands and grooves in the barrel throughout their length. If required clean the BARREL again.
7. Carbon fouling is removed with COMBINATION TOOL SCRAPERS and the NYLON PAD. Wipe clean the PISTON, GAS CYLINDER and GAS PLUG, then lightly oil.
8. Dry clean the whole weapon and examine it for damage etc.
9. Lightly oil the WEAPON and MAGAZINE, but NOT the SUSAT, or if fitted the IRON SIGHT APERTURES and POST.
10. Assemble the weapon and test for correct functioning. Put the SAFETY CATCH to FIRE **(F)**, operate the trigger, put the SAFETY CATCH to SAFE **(S)** and check that the CHANGE LEVER is at **'R'**.
11. **Cleaning of Susat**. Use NYLON BRUSH and oily swabs to remove debris from the SIGHT BRACKET, Avoid smearing oil on the RUBBER EYEPIECE. Dry clean the whole of the exterior of the SIGHT.

Blow away any dust from the LENSES. Using LENS CLEANING CLOTH or a TISSUE gently polish the LENSES with a circular motion, working from the centre of th LENS outwards. If stains or scratches are apparent report them to the Armourer. Lightly oil the SHOE, fit the SIGHT back onto the weapon if detached. SUSAT is to remain fitted for cleaning if applicable.

Conclusion

Provided you carry out the correct procedures for cleaning and preparation using the correct oils and lubricants the Rifle/LSW both perform reliably.

OPERATING IN ADVERSE CONDITIONS

Introduction

Hot, Dry, Sandy or Dusty Conditions
The types of weather conditions and their effects on the Rifle/LSW must be understood to be effectively dealt with.

Heat.

1. Overheating occurs more quickly.
2. Rust forms due to changes in temperatures.
3. Weapon accuracy can change with temperature.
4. Plastic parts on the Rifle can become distorted and damaged.
5. Metal parts may become very hot and unbearable to hold.

Penetration of Sand or Dust Sand or dust can quickly build up inside a Rifle. This can affect the moving parts and may stop them operating.

Solutions

Cleaning.

1. External surfaces should be properly dry-cleaned, all oil removed.
2. Internally clean as normal, but oil frequently, use issued lubricant.
3. Sufficient time must be made available the day before operations for weapons to be cleaned and re-oiled.

Spare Parts. These are easily lost in sand! In these conditions the LSW gunner would normally carry extra spare parts:

1. Bolt Carrier Assembly complete.
2. Firing Pin.
3. Firing Pin Retaining Pin.
4. Cam Stud.
5. Cocking Handle.

Procedures for Cleaning **Sand or Dust from a Weapon**

Weapon Stops or Will Not Fire, Bolt Forward. If the bolt cannot be freed by hand or will not operate freely, sand or dust may have jammed the locking splines. Therefore, carry out the following procedures:

1. Remove the magazine and holding the weapon with the magazine housing uppermost, apply oil to the underside of the bolt carrier whilst holding the muzzle down. Keep the muzzle down and allow a few seconds for the oil to seep into the barrel extension. Attempt to operate the bolt. Continue this action until the bolt frees.
2. Clean out the sand or dust from the splines and barrel extension using a cleaning brush, re-lubricate, reload and continue the action.

Muzzle and Dust Covers

The muzzle cover should be fitted at all times as this will prevent sand/dust from entering the barrel and jamming the locking splines. The dust cover should be kept closed at all times.

Magazines

Magazines normally filled with 30 rounds, in adverse conditons it may be wise to fill with less leaving space at the bottom of the MAGAZINE for sand or dust to collect. In these conditions it must be emptied out.

Overheating

Do not exceed the rates of fire with the Rifle/LSW. When possible the working parts should be cocked and held to the rear allowing cool air to circulate through the chamber and barrel.

HOT & WET CONDITIONS

Effects on Small Arms

Heat. This can take the form of a number of differing effects, which are:

1. Overheating will occur quicker in these conditions.
2. Weapon accuracy can change due to temperature variations.
3. Plastic parts on the weapon can become distorted and damaged.
4. Metal parts may become very hot and unbearable to hold.

Rust. Due to the fluctuations in temperature rust will form. It is a serious problem under these conditions.

Solutions

Lubrication. Up to plus 27c oil OX18 will prove to be effective. Over plus 27c Protective PX4 should be used.

Cleaning.

1. External surfaces should be cleaned and lubricated.
2. Internally Clean as normal internally as normal, oil more often, use the issued oil.
3. Inspect the all surfaces of the bolt and carrier assembly, upper receiver and chamber/barrel extension, check the TMH for rust, also pay close attention to the spring-loaded catches on the rifle.
4. Remove handprints and finger marks with a dry rag to prevent rust.
5. Cleaning and re-oiling throughout the day and before operations. No matter how much oil is used rust will form very quickly.
6. MAGAZINES must be unloaded and the insides checked for rust and moisture. AMMUNITION must be clean and dry before reloading.

7. The SUSAT LENSES can get *misted up* due to condensation making it difficult to see. Clear using a dry piece of rag or Army Form Blank.

Spare Parts. The following additional spares should be carried:

1. A complete BOLT CARRIER ASSEMBLY.
2. FIRING PIN
3. FIRING PIN RETAINING PIN
4. CAM STUD

Muzzle Covers. The muzzle cover should be fitted at all times as this will prevent sand/dust from entering the barrel and jamming the locking splines. The dust cover should be kept closed at all times.

Overheating. Do not exceed the rates of fire with the Rifle/LSW.

COLD AND EXTREME COLD WEATHER PROCEDURES

Introduction

Cold adverse weather conditions are referred to 'COLD' and 'EXTREME COLD CONDITIONS'. These conditions can be applied from NW Europe to the Arctic.

The range of temperatures are as follows:

a. Cold. 0°C to approximately minus 9°C.

b. Extreme Cold. Minus 9°C and below.

Cold Weather Effects on Small Arms

Cold. This can take the form of a number of differing effects, which are: Moisture on or in the weapon will freeze impairing the function. Moisture can be formed in a number of ways:

1. Directly from the change in the surrounding temperature.
2. Snow getting into or onto a hot weapon. Wet parts will quickly freeze as they cool.
3. Operations on water or snow may be in contact with the weapon.
4. Your breath on the optic sights will cause misting which will freeze.
5. Gloves or mittens reduces your handling skills increase the time taken to operate efficiently.
6. Plastic and metal parts become brittle and more likely to break or be damaged.

Freezing Rain. Is likely to interfere with correct operation.

Blizzard and Snow Snow getting into the weapon can build up, slowing down or stopping moving parts. The snow will melt on a hot weapon and on cooling will freeze all the moving parts together

Solutions

A number of preventative or remedial actions can be taken to help reduce the effects of cold or extreme cold weather.

Lubrication. The NATO lubricant 'LAW 0—157' is effective oil for these temperature ranges. It must only be used after all traces of other oils have been removed.

De-Icing. The de-icing of frozen moving parts, can be carried out by using wood alcohol 'AL-14 METHANOL'. Great care must be exercised when using it. Should it comes into contact with your skin it will rapidly induce frostbite.

Cleaning. Correct preparation for firing avoids a number of cold related problems. All traces of moisture are to be removed, using methanol as necessary; paying particular attention to the extractor and ejector and other small parts. Time must be made available to check weapons throughout the day before operations.

Spare Parts. LSW gunners should carry the following extra spares:

1. Bolt Carrier Assembly complete.
2. Firing Pin.
3. Firing Pin Retaining Pin.
4. Cam Stud.
5. Cocking Handle.

Procedures for Cleaning Ice from a Frozen Weapon

To clear ice, using methanol the following procedures should be applied.

Weapon Stops or Will Not Fire, Bolt Frozen Forward. If the bolt cannot be freed by hand or will not operate freely, ice may well have formed on the bolt carrier, bolt, bolt head and in particular the locking splines or barrel extension. Therefore, carry out the following procedures:

1. Apply methanol to the side of the bolt carrier holding the muzzle down. Leave for a few seconds and attempt to operate manually.
2. If weapon remains in a frozen, remove the MAGAZINE, (frozen to the weapon, use methanol to free it,) hold the weapon with MAGAZINE HOUSING uppermost apply methanol to the underside of the BOLT CARIER. Keep the weapon pointing down at an angle of 800 mils this will allow methanol to seep into the BARREL EXTENSION, after four seconds, attempt to operate the BOLT. Continue this action until the BOLT operates freely. Reload, cock and continue the action.

Weapon Stops or Will Not Fire, Trigger Mechanism Frozen.

If on trying to operate the TRIGGER, it will not move, or when operated the HAMMER will not work the probable cause is the TRIGGER MECHANISM or parts are frozen, if so, carry out the following drill:

1. Keep weapon pointing in a safe direction.
2. Apply methanol through the COCKING HANDLE slot to free the moving parts of the TRIGGER MECHANISM, after four seconds attempt to operate the TRIGGER.

WARNING: *A round will be fired if the mechanism has been freed.*

3. Should this not resolve the problem the weapon must be unloaded, the TMH removed, and methanol applied directly to the frozen parts.

Frozen External Parts. Should external parts of the weapon such as the SAFETY CATCH, CHANGE LEVER, MAGAZINE RELEASE CATCH or SUSAT RANGE DRUM become inoperative due to ice, directly apply methanol to dissolve the ice bringing frozen parts back into use.

Dry Functioning (Hand operating the mechanism)

The need for clearing light icing, or the use of methanol can be by unloading and dry functioning the weapon (hand operating the mechanism several times). Obviously this will only be carried out as and when the tactical situation allows, i.e., prior to a patrol, before taking over as a sentry or stand-to, etc.

A frozen DUST COVER will not operate when the recoiling COCKING HANDLE hits it, causing a stoppage or breaking the cover as well as possibly affecting other parts of the weapon.

Dry functioning will free a frozen cover and avoid these problems.

Magazine Changing

The use of mittens makes it difficult to open both types of pouches in service, and extract magazines. It should be considered necessary to place the magazines into extra haversacks.

SUSAT

The SUSAT performs well throughout different climatic conditions in spite of which the following points are made:

1. After any action or activity that brings the sight into contact with snow, the field of view may have been reduced by snow build up on the lenses.
2. In extreme cold conditions, the effects of smoke and ice fog around a group of weapons when they are fired, can create a mist in front of the

SUSAT. This may obscure a target if indistinct or at a distance.
The trained Soldier in this situation would continue with the EBS until a clear target picture is available.

3. Under these conditions should a firer breathe on the rear lens of the SUSAT the condensation will freeze, creating a thin film of ice can be quickly cleared by the use of a gloved finger, although this will in time cause smearing.

Muzzle Cover

In these conditions an efficient MUZZLE COVER is essential. A minor modification to the standard issued cover can be made by threading a thin twine or wire through it, tying the MUZZLE COVER to the RIFLE BARREL preventing its loss.

DESCRIPTION OF AMMUNITION

It is obvious that you must be able to immediately recognise different types of ammunition that you will be using. Especially when you are filling a MAGAZINE - under pressure - with loose rounds or using a CHARGER.
The weapons fire rimless 5.56mm ammunition. The manufacturers information is stamped on the base of each cartridge.
Ammunition is normally supplied in cardboard cartons of 20 rounds or in bandoliers containing a CHARGER and 150 ROUNDS in clips of 10 ROUNDS.

TYPES OF AMMUNITION.

There are four types of ammunition issued, they are as follows:-

BALL - This has a smooth brass cartridgecase, a jacketed bullet with a GREEN TIP and percussion cap in the base.

TRACER - Similar to BALL rounds with a GREEN & RED painted tip.

BLANK - This round has a brass case but no bullet. The top of the case is closed by crimping.

DRILL - A silver coloured grooved case, a copper jacketed bullet and no percussion cap.

CARE OF AMMUNITION.

Always look after ammunition; keep it clean, dry and free from oil. Never let it lie in the direct rays of the sun as this can cause inaccuracies when firing.
Do NOT use a round as a tool.
Do NOT apply pressure to the base of a round, either with a clip or another round.
There is a possibility of detonating the percussion cap and thereby firing the round.
Tampering with ammunition is dangerous and strictly forbidden.
MAGAZINES are to be inspected regularly. Damaged MAGAZINES will cause stoppages.

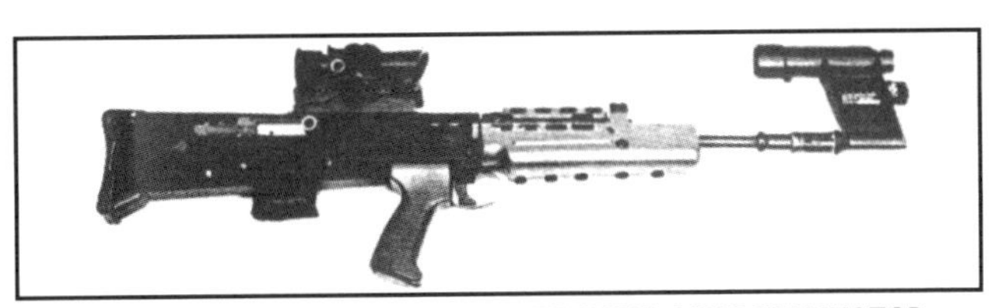

5.56 RIFLE SUSAT SIGHT FITTED WITH SMALL ARMS COLLIMATOR

THE SMALL ARMS COLLIMATOR (SAC)

SAC provides a method of boresighting (zeroing) that can be carried out by day or night. There is no need to strip the weapon, saving time, ammunition and valuable range time.
It allows you to record your zero by day or night and regain that zero - that is if you are sufficiently trained and skilled to use it.
Having used the SAC, when you fire your PW/LSW with the target correctly sighted YOU WILL get a hit. This will have been achieved without having fired a shot to zero your weapon.
The need for accuracy has become more important by the growing use of optical and night vision sights which are more

FITTING AN SAC TO A LSW

sensitive to rough handling than iron sights and therefore need more frequent checking and setting.

It goes without saying your weapons need to be zeroed correctly at all times irrespective of the duties or operations you are engaged in.

Your ability to use the SAC is without doubt a great advantage for you to be confident that your weapon is correctly zeroed. Any deviation from the average zero position can be recorded to give a personal check zero position for each firer. This approach will improve accuracy over using an average standard reference position.

CARE & HANDLING

The Collimator, Small Arms, LIA1 is a sealed unit and **no attempt** must be made to adjust or strip any component beyond that as instructed.

The Spigot must not be damaged in any way.

SAFETY and MAINTENANCE

WARNING

THIS EQUIPMENT CONTAINS A GASEOUS TRITIUM LIGHT SOURCE (GTLS), THEREFORE THE INSTRUCTIONS NOT TO ADJUST OR STRIP THE **SAC** WILL BE STRICTLY OBSERVED.

IMMEDIATE ACTIONS TO BE TAKEN ON DISCOVERY OF A DAMAGED GTLS ARE AS FOLLOWS:-

1. DO NOT TOUCH THE GTLS.
2. DO NOT INHALE THE ESCAPING GAS.
3. VENTILATE AND EVACUATE THE AREA.
4. INFORM THE APPOINTED RADIATION PROTECTION SUPERVISOR.
5. WASH HANDS THOROUGHLY, DO NOT USE SOAP.

BRIEF DESCRIPTION

The Collimator Small Arms Cased, LIA1, consists of Collimator, Small Arms, LIA1, (SAC) and Confidence Checker housed in a moulded case for transit purposes. Also included in the case are a small pack of lens cleaning tissue.

The SAC is an optical/mechanical instrument that comprises an anodised aluminium alloy casting which houses the optical collimator assembly in which the graticule pattern is contained.

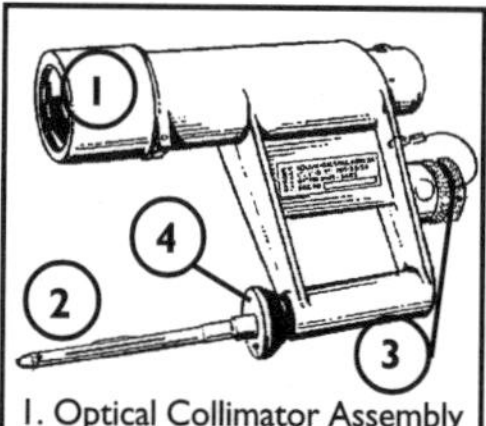

1. Optical Collimator Assembly
2. Spigot. 3. Betalight Assembly
4. Bumper Rubber

The optical collimator assembly is mounted to the upper body of the device whilst the lower body provides a mounting for the sprung steel spigot. The spigot is designed to precisely fit the 5.56mm barrel and the forward end of the spigot is equipped with a bumper rubber to ensure correct insertion. The body of the SAC also provides a housing for the graticule illumination assembly (Betalight Assembly) which is required when using an unfiltered CWS or IWS.

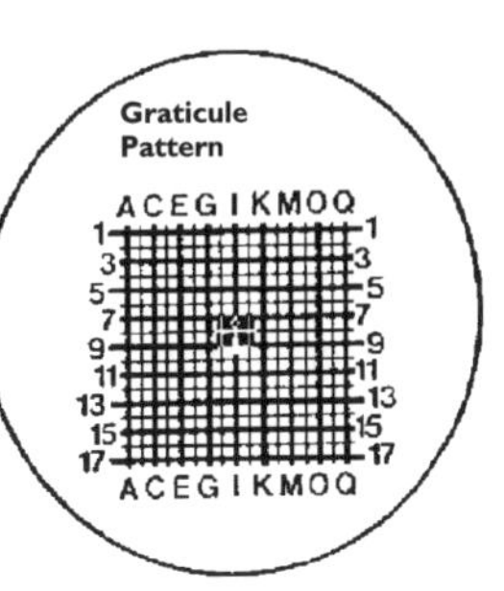

OPERATING INSTRUCTIONS

In order to achieve accurate results the following procedure should be carried out in a prone supported firing position. It is VERY important that the left hand is not used to grip the hand-guard but should simply support the rifle. The help of a 'buddy' is required to enable adjustment of the sight.

To use the SAC proceed as follows:

1. Apply a light coating of oil to the shaft of the spigot.
2. Ensure rifle is unloaded, carry out NSP normal safety precautions
3. Adopt the prone supported firing position.
4. Your 'buddy' should fit the SAC by pushing the spigot into the rifle muzzle until the flash eliminator is in contact with the bumper rubber. You check that the graticule pattern is upright. Your 'buddy' carefully rotates the SAC back and forth and finally to the upright position, this will have the effect of settling the spigot in the bore of the rifle and will result in a more accurate reading.
5. If boresighting, you tell your 'buddy' to adjust the sights until the pointer exactly corresponds with the boresighting datum. The boresighting datum is the point where the horizontal line **9** and the vertical line **I** intersect as shown in the illustration on the right.
6. If simply recording a reading after zeroing by live firing you should note as accurately as possible the position of the sight pointer on the graticule pattern

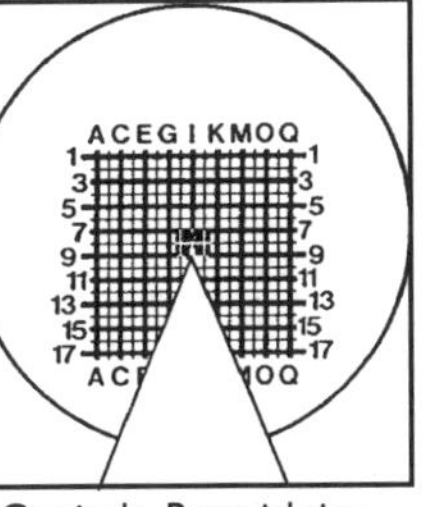

Graticule Boresighting mark using SUSAT

Recording Zero

In the example on the left it shows the correct zero position is F5 (using SUSAT)

7. When checking zero you simply note the position of the pointer and if necessary ask your 'buddy' to adjust the sight until the previously recorded setting is achieved.
8. It is most important that after the sight has been adjusted the SAC is removed and replaced by your 'buddy' so that you may again check that the sight relationship is correct. It is often the case that when the lock nuts on the horizontal adjustment screws of the SUSAT are tightened the sight moves slightly in direction. Careful checking at this stage will ensure an accurate result.
9. Remove the SAC and replace in transit case.
10. Make careful note of the graticule readings.

Night Sights

When using the SAC with CWS the tip of the inverted V on the CWS graticule should be used instead of the pointer and in the case of the IWS the top of the upper vertical bar. When operating CWS or IWS without the daylight filter in place it will be necessary to remove the Betalight assembly from its housing and screw it into the forward end of the optical assembly in order to illuminate the graticule. When carrying out boresighting or checking in dusk or equivalent conditions it will be necessary to shroud the sight and operate with the filter removed in order to discern the graticule. A poncho or shelter sheet draped over you and your 'buddy' will protect the sight from the otherwise high light level.

Checking Alignment

Each SAC is equipped with a confidence checker which is carried in the transit case. This device enables you to carry out a simple check to ensure that the spigot is still correctly aligned to the graticule. The confidence checker consists of a shaped device through which two holes are drilled. The larger hole at the bottom of the checker will accept the SAC spigot and the smaller hole at the top of the checker is designed as a viewing hole. In order to check the alignment push the spigot into the larger hole of the checker until the device butts

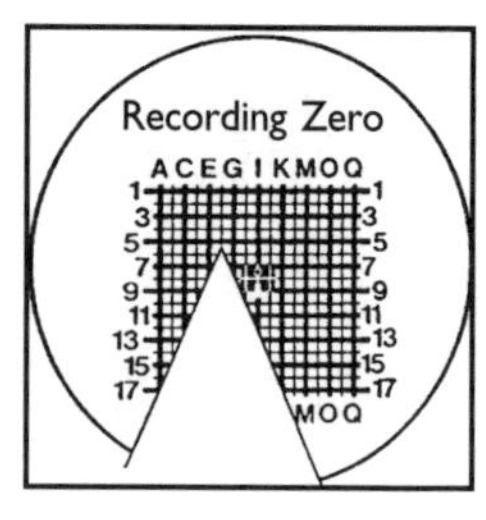

against the optical assembly of the SAC. Ensure the confidence checker is upright and look through the viewing hole. If the complete circle encompassing the graticule pattern can be discerned the SAC alignment is correct. If it is not possible to discern the circle around the graticule pattern the complete equipment is to be handed to the unit armourer for checking. The only maintenance you are permitted to carry out on the SAC is limited to cleaning.

CLEANING

There are no special tools required. Standard lens cleaning tissue, contained in the case, should be used to clean the objective lens.

If there is mud or grit on the objective lens, it should be removed with clean water.

Soap or weak detergent may be used to remove grease stains or smears.

The body of the SAC is similarly cleaned. Entrapped debris may be removed by loosening the dirt with a soft bristled brush.

Total submersion of the SAC is to be avoided.

Replacement of parts, to be carried out by Unit Armourers, is limited to:-

Replacement of the Betalight Assembly.

Replacement of the Bumper Rubber.

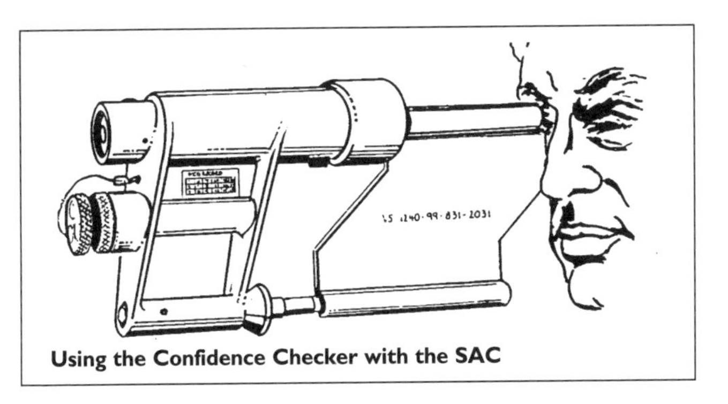

Using the Confidence Checker with the SAC

AIMING WITH THE IRON SIGHT

1. With both your eyes open identify the target and roughly align the weapon adjusting the body position so that the weapon points naturally at the target without effort.

2. Position your cheek on the CHEEK PIECE so that the eye is approximately 25mm from the APERTURE.

3. Look through the centre of the APERTURE and centralise the TIP of the FORESIGHT. The BACKSIGHT will be too close to the eye for the edges of the aperture to be clearly seen; however a clear area in the centre of the aperture will be apparent.

Ensure that the FORESIGHT is upright and clearly in focus. Keep the left eye open.

4. It may be necessary to move your head slightly in order to achieve SIGHT ALIGNMENT; it is essential, however, once it has been achieved, that the position of your head remains unchanged.

5. Maintaining this alignment, focus on the tip of the foresight lining it up with the target or more correctly called the POINT of AIM (POA), this completes the 'AIM PICTURE'. You will find that when doing this the target will become blurred for a few moments.

6. Check that the tip of the FORESIGHT is still in the centre of the aperture

7. The adjustment of your sights can give you a more 'COMFORTABLE AIM PICTURE' or eye relief, you must test and if necessary adjust your sights with the aid of your instructor. This will help you to be consistent with your aim and improve your results.

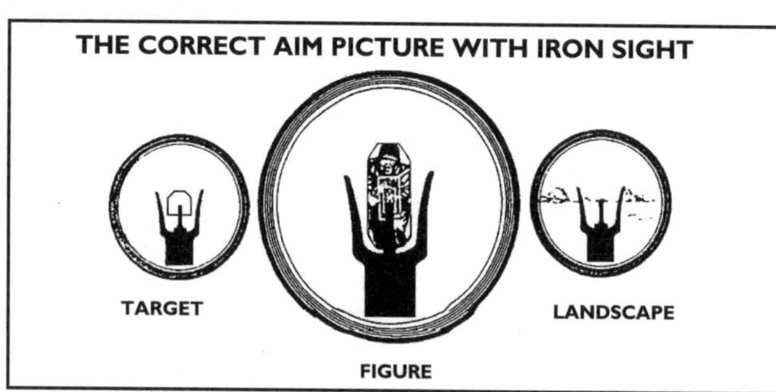

THE CORRECT AIM PICTURE WITH SUSAT SIGHT

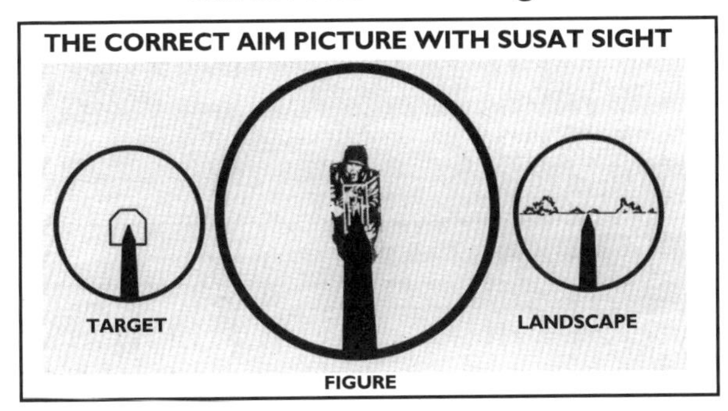

IF after GENUINE attempts you are unable to aim keeping BOTH EYES OPEN, you should close the left eye. The 'BOTH EYES OPEN' technique is generally recommended as better with the IRON SIGHT.

AIMING WITH THE SUSAT

Look along the barrel with both eyes open, select the target and roughly align the weapon on the target. Look through the EYEPIECE with your disengaged eye, resting your eyebrow against the rubber EYEPIECE.

Focus the POINTER of your sight until it is clear in your vision. Keep the POINTER upright, align the TIP of the POINTER with your POA - Point Of AIM, ensure that you have a CLEAR - CIRCULAR view through the SIGHT LENS.

Sighting View

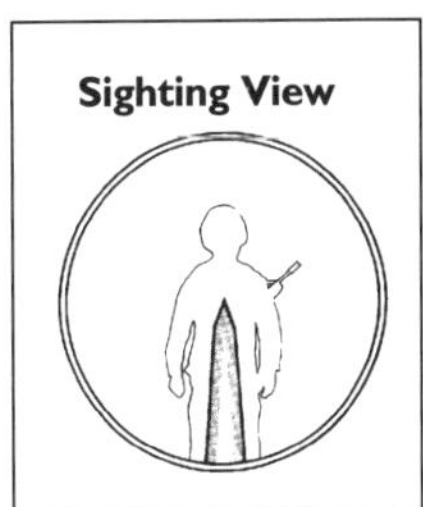

AIMING WITH THE EBS - EMERGENCY BATTLE SIGHT.

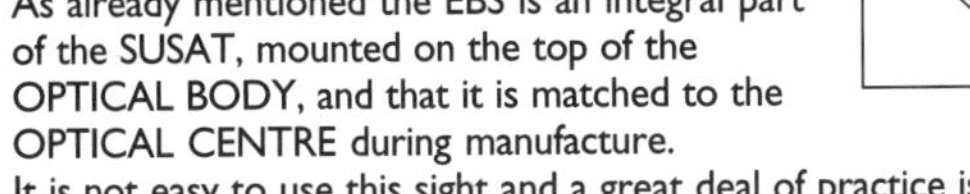

As already mentioned the EBS is an integral part of the SUSAT, mounted on the top of the OPTICAL BODY, and that it is matched to the OPTICAL CENTRE during manufacture.

It is not easy to use this sight and a great deal of practice is required to become skilled at getting the CORRECT ALIGNMENT with the weapon and at the same time finding the CORRECT AIM PICTURE.

The position of the EBS means that you have to adopt a different position with your CHEEK or the EYEPIECE of the SUSAT will interfere with your eye when aiming.

Skill at Arms & Shooting

The 'Rules for Aiming' with the EBS are very simple and are as follows:-

1. Look over the top of the SUSAT and roughly align the MUZZLE of the weapon with the target.

2. Close your disengaged eye and look through the APERTURE BACKSIGHT of the EBS.

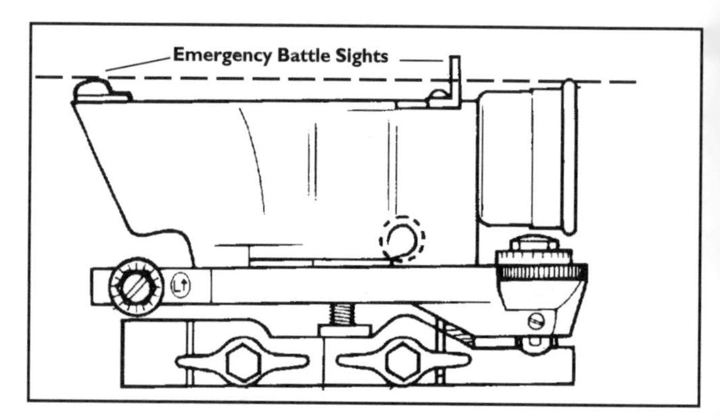

3. Align the tip of the EBS FORESIGHT BLADE in the centre of the APERTURE, keeping the SIGHTS UPRIGHT.

4. Focus on the TIP of the FORESIGHT, Align it on your POINT OF AIM on the target at the same time maintaining the TIP of the FORESIGHT in the CENTRE of the APERTURE.

NOTE: You may have difficulty in 'focusing' and the Target may appear blurred and if you have your eye too far away from the APERTURE it will appear too small to see through.

As already pointed out it is only with practice that you will become accustomed to your EBS . If it is any consolation to you, this was the type of sight used with great effect by your predecessors.

USE OF COVER - MUZZLE CLEARANCE.

The diagram on the following page is produced to make you aware of the fact that your LINE of SIGHT - the dotted line - on the weapon is high in relation to the AXIS of the BORE of the BARREL or the FLIGHT PATH of the BULLET when fired.

Firing from behind low cover it may well be possible/essential to have a clear LINE of SIGHT to the target, but, at the same time have the FLIGHT PATH of the BULLET obstructed by the cover. Obstruction may be less noticeable a few metres in front of the position than directly in front of the MUZZLE.
It is therefore important to always be mindful of the MUZZLE CLEARANCE and make allowances for it when selecting a FIRE POSITION, at the same time consider the possible increased exposure to view.

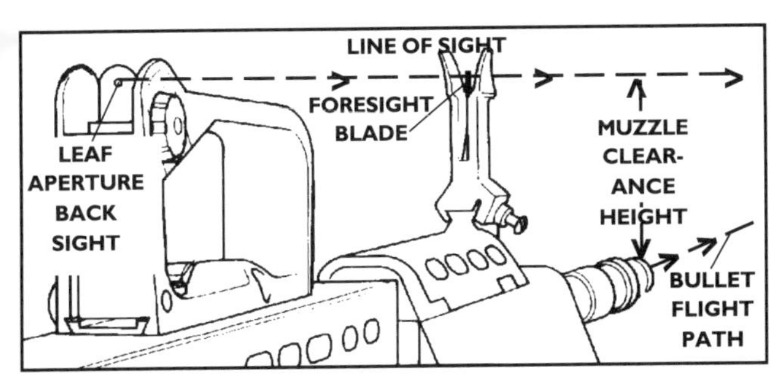

SETTINGS & ADJUSTMENTS.

Zeroing the Weapon The purpose of zeroing is to superimpose the true position of the MEAN POINT of IMPACT (MPI) on the CORRECT ZERO POSITION so that with the appropriate setting and use of wind allowance, a group of shots fired will form centrally at all of the ranges selected.
To determine the true position of the MPI, you should fire a number of shots, not less than 20, at the same AIMING MARK and under the same conditions.
You must be capable of consistently firing five rounds at 100 metres and achieving an average of 150mm group using the SUSAT sight or a 200mm group using an IRON SIGHT. It is essential for you to zero your own weapon for the following reasons:-

1. Variations in your aiming.
2. The effect of 'weapon jump', influenced by your physical build .
3. The firing position you adopt for your own comfort.
4. The control you have, dictated by the way you hold the weapon.

Skill at Arms & Shooting

Zeroing should be carried out:-

1. When you are initially issued with the weapon.
2. Before and, whenever possible, during active service.
3. If the sights are changed.
4. When there is any doubt of the weapons accuracy.

ZEROING RANGE.

The ideal range for zeroing is 100 metres, which combines clarity of aim with lack of wind effect.

A range of 25 metres may be used if a 100 metre range is not available.

CORRECT ZERO POSITION (CZP)

The correct positions of the MPI in relation to the POINT of AIM (POA) at 100 metres and at 25 metres, with sight settings shown are as below:-

Weapon	Sight	Sight Setting	CZP	
			100 metres	25 metres
Rifle	SUSAT	300 metres	90mm above	22mm below POA
	Iron	200 metres	100mm above	25mm below POA
LSW	SUSAT	300 metres	80mm above	20mm below POA
	Iron	200 metres	100 above	25mm below POA

If the MPI obtained does not coincide with the CZP given above, then the sights of the weapon require adjustment.

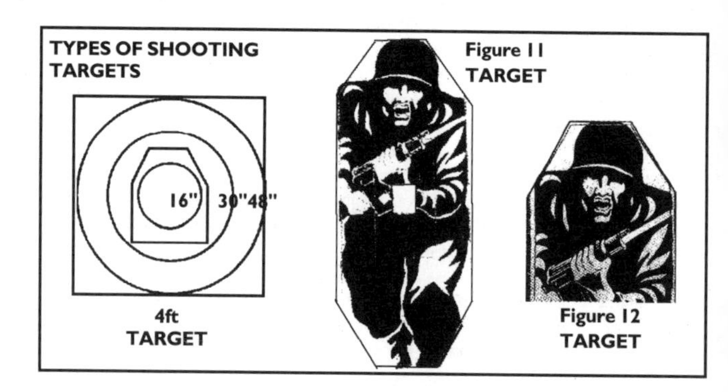

Figure 11 TARGET

Figure 12 TARGET

SIGHT ADJUSTMENT

The sights of the weapon are adjustable for elevation and for direction. The Combination Tool should be used to make these adjustments.

ELEVATION - see diagram below

To move the MPI up, turn the VERTICAL ADJUSTMENT NUT in the direction indicated by the arrow marked 'U'. To move the MPI down turn the ADJUSTER in the direction indicated by arrow 'D'.

One graduation moves the MPI approximately 13mm vertically at 25 metres or 50mm at 100 metres.

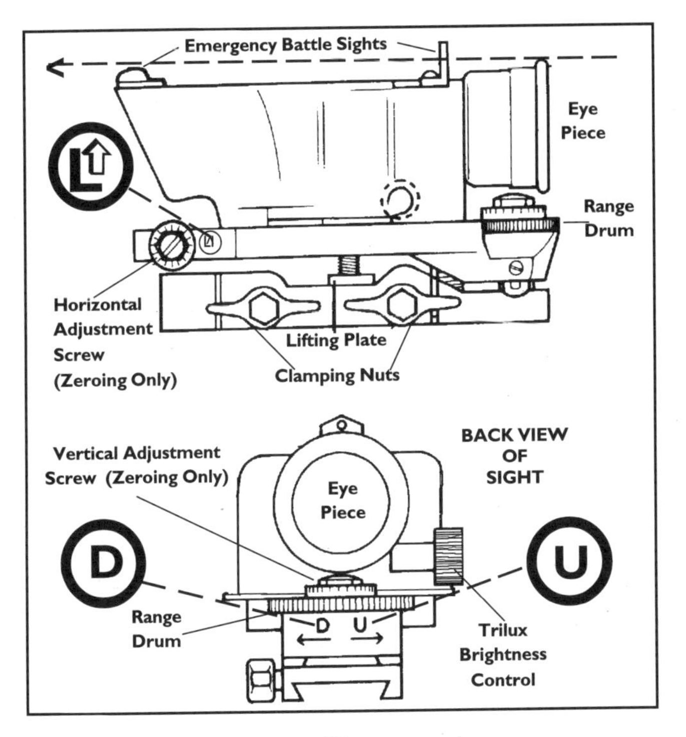

DIRECTION.

To move the MPI to the left, loosen the LOCK-NUT and turn the HORIZONTAL ADJUSTER SCREW in the direction as shown by the arrow 'L' as illustrated in the diagram on the previous page.
To move the MPI to the right turn the ADJUSTER as shown by the arrow 'R' - **on the opposite side of the SIGHT BASE.**
When the required adjustment has been made, turn the opposite ADJUSTMENT SCREW against the direction of its arrow, then tighten the LOCK-NUTS.
One graduation moves the MPI approximately 13mm horizontally at 25 metres or 50mm at 100 metres.

IRON SIGHT

ELEVATION. To move the MPI up, depress the LOCKING PLUNGER on the FORESIGHT, using the COMBINATION TOOL, then rotate the

VERTICAL ADJUSTMENT SCREW in the direction as indicated by the arrow 'U. To move the MPI down, turn the SCREW in the direction of arrow 'D'. One graduation will raise or lower the MPI approximately 13mm at 25 metres or 50mm at 100 metres.
DIRECTION. To move the MPI to the left, depress the LOCKING PLUNGER on the HORIZONTAL ADJUSTMENT SCREW, using the COMBINATION TOOL, turn the screw in the direction as indicated by the arrow **'L'** (see diagram on previous page).
To move the MPI to the right turn the screw in the opposite direction.
One graduation moves the MPI horizontally approximately 13mm at 25 metres or 50mm at 100 metres.

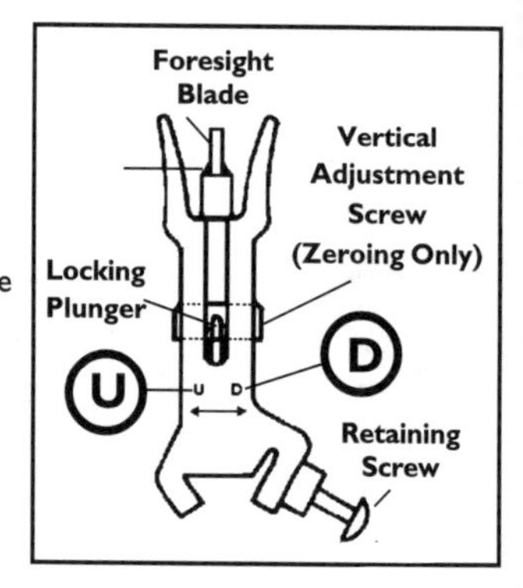

EYE RELIEF ADJUSTMENT.

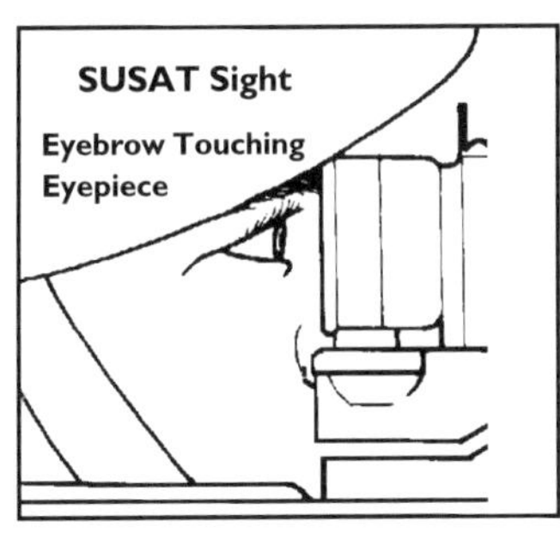

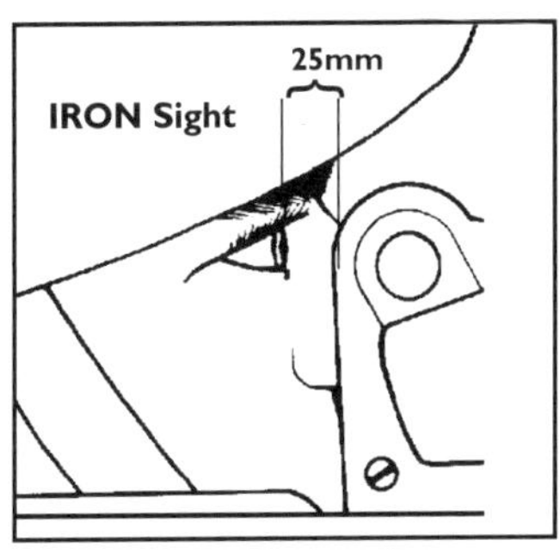

To adjust either the SUSAT or the IRON SIGHT to obtain the CORRECT EYE RELIEF carry out the following:-

1. Loosen the CLAMPING NUTS/ SCREWS.
2. Operate the LIFTING PLATE (SUSAT), or unscrew the RETENTION STUD (IRON SIGHT), and slide the SIGHT forward or backward as required.
3. Adjust the SIGHT so that the RETENTION STUD is located in the hole in the SIGHT RAIL that gives you the best possible EYE RELIEF.
4. Tighten the CLAMPING NUTS/ SCREWS.
5. Optimum EYE RELIEF is achieved by moving the position of your head.

FIRE CONTROL

As a Rifleman in action you would normally carry six full magazines, one on your weapon and five in pouches. You would also be carrying a bandolier containing 150 rounds which is worn slung over your equipment. It is used to re-supply the LSW or to refill your own magazines during a lull in operations.

You may also be issued with TRACER ROUNDS for use with the LSW or used for target indication. It is important to always keep in mind the conservation of all supplies, especially ammunition. The high rates of fire that are possible must be strictly controlled at all times.

This can be achieved by good Fire Discipline and Fire Control Orders indicating the "types of fire" to be used in battle.

Skill at Arms & Shooting

DESCRIPTION OF TYPES OF FIRE.

DELIBERATE.

A slow rate of fire not more than 10 rounds per minute. The order usually given after the FIRE FIGHT is won to prevent the enemy returning accurate fire, or from observing your dispositions or moving from their own positions. Always count the rounds you fire to know how many you have left in your magazine.
The FIRE ORDER will be on the assumption you're "READY", been given the RANGE, and TARGET INDICATED; is - "FIRE".
When ordered to "STOP", SAFETY CATCH to **'S'**, change MAGAZINE if necessary, adopt ALERT position, observe, await further orders. If ordered - "GO ON", put your SAFETY CATCH to **'F'** and carry on firing.

SNAP SHOOTING.

This is shooting when a target appears for just a short time. If you are a skilled shot you should get off two accurate shots at the target.
The FIRE ORDER - as you are awaiting the appearance of the target - will be - "WATCH and SHOOT".
When given the command "STOP" and "GO ON" your actions are as for DELIBERATE SHOOTING

RAPID FIRE.

Principally used in order to WIN the 'FIRE FIGHT' or when any number of the enemy are attacking your position. It is not wildly firing at random, but carefully aimed shots to makes every one count. Firing must be strictly controlled to ensure that no more ammunition is used than necessary to achieve the desired result.
You should, provided you are a skilled soldier, be able to get off 20 well aimed shots in a minute at several targets.
With RAPID FIRE practice you should develop a rhythm of operation with your weapon, this in turn will help with your breathing control, correct aim, holding and trigger operation. Your "follow through" will be carried out as a natural and correct sequence.
With practice, shallow breaths between shots during RAPID FIRE and breath restraint can result in being able to 'get off' two or three shots. Care should be exercised not to cause undue strain.
The FIRE ORDER after, the RANGE and TARGET has been indicated, is in two parts:- "RAPID" - "FIRE" - one after the other.
On the command "RAPID" check CHANGE LEVER is at `**R'** and aim at target.

On the command "FIRE", you fire as fast as possible with well aimed accurate shots, moving from one target to another as each one falls. Continue to fire until there are no targets to fire at or you given the order to "STOP".
Counting the rounds and changing MAGAZINES must be carried out as for DELIBERATE FIRE.
After continuous fire, allow the weapon to cool at any a lull in the firing by COCKING it, and engaging the HOLDING OPEN CATCH, thus clearing the breech, allowing air to circulate. If you didn't catch the ejected ROUND - clean it - and put it in your pouch or a magazine. If ordered to "GO ON", operate the BOLT RELEASE and continue to fire.

AUTOMATIC FIRE.

Used mostly in close quarters battle, especially during the final stages of an assault, or springing an ambush, or when faced by a mass attack. Used to great effect in house clearing, clearing trenches bunkers and woodlands. It is the responsibility of your Section Commander to decide on the rate/volume of fire - dependent upon the ammunition available. You are also to use your initiative in the effective use and conservation of ammunition.
The FIRE ORDER given will be "BURSTS" - "RAPID" - "FIRE". On the command "BURSTS" the CHANGE LEVER is set to **`A'** and on "FIRE", fire in short burst of two to three rounds.
The actions you carry out on the order: "STOP" and "GO ON" are the same as for RAPID firing.

FIGHTING at CLOSE QUARTERS.

Firing at Targets Crossing your front. Under operational conditions the majority of shots fired will be against moving targets at short ranges, a proportion of them will be crossing your front. The target they present will move quickly from cover to cover, with the least amount of exposure for the shortest possible time. You must develop quick reactions and anticipate the moves that the enemy will make.
This coupled with the ability to develop techniques to "out wit" and engage the enemy, making every round count.
While moving across close country or through an urban area you will often be adopting different positions to fire from, standing, kneeling, sitting or lying.
This will test your ability to react quickly and fire accurately under such

conditions when engaging a moving target. Again, it will only be with constant practice that you will develop the skills required and to maintain a high state of readiness.

Making allowances for a Crossing Target.

When you fire at a moving target its movement continues across your front during the time it takes the bullet to reach it. An allowance for this must be made by you "aiming off" in front of the target. If you don't the shots will miss by passing behind it.
Aiming in front so as to make allowances for the movement of the target is known as the "LEAD".
Depending upon the speed at which the target is moving, will be the amount of "LEAD" that you will have to allow to make a hit. To make it more difficult - the target may be moving obliquely - at a angle across your front.
All that can be offered to you in this case is - only with practice at such a target will you be able to develop the right 'touch' or 'technique' when firing at moving targets.
Obviously targets at longer ranges are much more difficult to hit. Should you be using an IRON SIGHT with the a target beyond 300 metres you will need to aim higher than normal. If you are using
a SUSAT sight you will need to increase the range setting, while maintaining the normal elevation.

METHODS OF ENGAGING DIRECT & OBLIQUE CROSSING TARGETS.

As previously explained, crossing targets are successfully hit when the correct amount of LEAD has been taken into consideration and your POINT of AIM has been adjusted and applied to the target.
There are several methods used for engaging moving targets they are explained over page:-

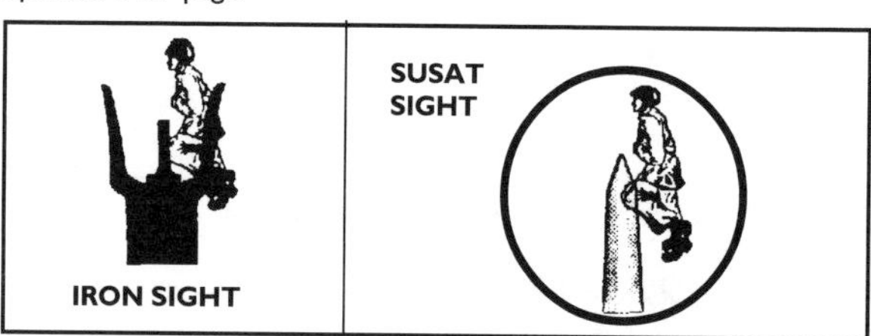

Skill at Arms & Shooting

The BASIC Method

Aim behind the target, swing through the target to the leading edge as in the illustration above. Do not check the swing, open fire and if required increase or decrease the 'LEAD' while firing several shots, continue to fire until the target is hit or disappears.

The AMBUSH Method

Used when it is difficult to follow or swing with the target, especially when you are in the prone or sitting position with perhaps both elbows rested. You select a POINT OF AIM on its anticipated route, ahead of the target, come into the aim, wait for the target to appear, start firing just before the target reaches your selected POA. Continue until it is hit, or disappears or if you know that you have missed it - in which case the target has moved ahead of your POA, in other words you need more practice!!

The SHOT GUN Method

Favoured by those who are experienced and successful 'poachers'. Under operational conditions very often there is not time nor space to use your sights, therefore with BOTH EYES open, look only at the TARGET, keep your head up, left hand gripping firmly and well forward, weapon pointing naturally at the target - 'FIRE' - all in one action.
Speed and accuracy are the basis of this technique, which can be very effective up to 150 metres.

FIRING BURSTS.

In certain situations automatic fire can be very effective. In situations such as ambushes, house clearing and night fighting, When operating in these conditions and in anticipation of action your CHANGE LEVER would be set at **'A'**.
Normally and in fact the most accurate position is to fire from the shoulder. You can obviously fire your weapon in any position provided it is held correctly, you are comfortable with it and you get the right results.
Remember:-

1. With the Rifle it has a tendency to 'climb' as you fire a burst, therefore - AIM LOWER, it might be better to get off several well aimed shots.
2. If firing BURSTS , remember, SHORT BURSTS - of TWO or THREE rounds.
3. Don't get caught out with an empty MAGAZINE - change it.
4. DON'T attempt to fire from the HIP - you will become a casualty through the COCKING HANDLE hitting your RIGHT ARM.

"DON'T WASTE AMMUNITION - SOMEONE HAS TO CARRY IT"

Skill at Arms & Shooting

TEST QUESTIONS

1. Parts of Gas System should be cleaned & gauged after firing ..... rounds
2. What is the SAC used for
3. What is the "Bore Sighting Datum"
4. On discovering a damaged GTLS what IA is to be taken
5. How is a "Confidence Checker" used and what for.
6. What replacement parts on the SAC are carried out by the Armourer
7. What is "Eye Relief"
8. How near should your eye be to the Aperture of the Iron Sight
9. Should you aim with the Iron Sight with both eyes open
10. Aiming with SUSAT "focus pointer until clear vision".....complete drill
11. Name the five rules of aiming with the EBS
12. What do you understand by "Muzzle Clearance"
13. When should Zeroing take place
14. What is the ideal range for Zeroing
15. What are the reference number for figure targets
16. SUSAT Sight. One graduation moves MPI ....at 100m.

Skill at Arms & Shooting

5.56 RIFLE & LSW TRAINING TESTS

PURPOSE OF TRAINING TESTS

You have to be fully trained and highly skilled with your personal weapons at all times. It is only with practice that you will attain a high standard and only with regular practice that you will maintain those high standards and pass your Annual Personal Weapons Test first time. Don't miss any opportunity to take part in firing practices it will help you to achieve this aim.

These tests will enable your instructors to assess your safety standards, handling and application of fire with both weapons. You are required to be regularly tested under a variety of conditions. This will give your examiners a good measure of how well you have been trained.

The tests are used to assess your standards with either the Rifle or the LSW, it is not necessary for you to be tested on both weapons.

TEST No 1 SAFETY

Conditions. The weapon will be laid on the ground, with a MAGAZINE fitted, LOADED, SAFETY CATCH NOT APPLIED the CHANGE LEVER at **'R'** will be told to PICK UP the rifle, you should: pick up the weapon, put the SAFETY CATCH to **'S'**,

take off the MAGAZINE and check that there is no ROUND in the CHAMBER. You will then be told to hand it to the examiner. When doing so you must carry out the following:-

1. Pick it up with the MUZZLE POINTING in a SAFE direction.
2. Check that the SAFETY CATCH to **'S'**.
3. Cock weapon, operate the HOLDING OPEN CATCH, check it yourself, then show - "prove it" to the examiner, that the BODY, CHAMBER and BOLT FACE are clear. EASE SPRINGS, and hand over the weapon to the examiner.

ASSESSMENT.

You will ONLY Pass this test if you carry out ALL the safety precautions and actions correctly.

TEST No 2 PREPARATION FOR FIRING - CLEANING

Conditions: Weapon with MAGAZINE. Cleaning Tool Roll, Flannelette and Oil.

1. Strip the weapon - including the SLING - as you have been taught for daily cleaning.

2. Dry clean the whole of the weapon, looking out for any damage.

3. Lightly oil the WORKING SURFACES of the BOLT, GUIDE RODS and CAM STUD.

4. Put the weapons together and test that it functions correctly.

5. Re - fit the sling.

ASSESSMENT

Standards: The main purpose is to test your ability to strip and assemble the weapon correctly. No time limit is set for this test. Skilled - up to two mistakes made. Average - three or four mistakes made. Fail - over four mistakes. You will only pass this test if **NO** mistakes are made that affect SAFETY PRECAUTIONS or ACTIONS.

TEST No 3 MAGAZINE FILLING - this is a timed test.

Conditions: MAGAZINE CHARGER , MAGAZINE. and 30 ROUNDS in clips On the order "GO", using an EMPTY MAGAZINE, you will fill it with 30 ROUNDS.

a. Filling by using the CHARGER.

b. Filling by HAND.

Leave the MAGAZINE filled ready for the next test.

ASSESSMENT.

a. Standards: With the CHARGER. Skilled - 20 sec. Average - 21 to 30 sec. Fail - over 30 sec. b. By HAND. Skilled - 60 seconds or less. Average - 61 to 75 sec. Fail - over 75 sec.

TEST No 4 LOADING - STANDING POSITION - a timed test

Conditions. Put ONE FULL MAGAZINE in a fastened POUCH. On the order "LOAD", timing will commence until you have completed the LOAD. Your POUCH must be FASTENED - the time taken to do this is NOT included in the time limit.

ASSESSMENT.

Standards 1. SKILLED - 10 seconds or less. AVERAGE - 11 to 15 seconds. FAIL - over 15 seconds. 2. TWO SECONDS will be added to your total time for each mistake.

You will only pass this test if **NO** mistakes are made that affect SAFETY PRECAUTIONS or ACTIONS. NOTE: The weapon is left LOADED ready for the next test.

TEST No 5 GAS STOPPAGE & IMMEDIATE ACTIONS (IA's)

Conditions: This test is only concerned with IA's and GAS STOPPAGES. NO time limit, but all actions must be carried out correctly and efficiently.

1. Using the LOADED weapon from the previous test, the order given will be :- "Down - Ready - Test and Adjust - Rapid Fire".

2. Order "weapon firing alright - weapon stops", you examine position of the COCKING HANDLE. Order given "Not fully to the rear", on examination of the BODY and CHAMBER, Order "ROUNDS in MAGAZINE, CHAMBER clear. You will be allowed to complete the drill and fire. Then given the order "weapon fires one or two ROUNDS and stops again" - "NOT fully to the rear" - "ROUNDS in the MAGAZINE, CHAMBER clear".

3. You should operate the BOLT RELEASE, apply the SAFETY CATCH and using the COMBINATION TOOL, adjust the GAS REGULATOR.

4. The test is not complete until the SAFETY CATCH is set at 'F', the weapon re-aimed and the TRIGGER operated.

5. You will then be given the order "STOP".

ASSESSMENT

1. Standards: Skilled - All actions correct. Average - One or two mistakes. Fail more than two mistakes.
2. You will only pass this test if NO mistakes are made that affect SAFETY PRECAUTIONS or ACTIONS.

TEST No 6 UNLOADING - LYING POSITION - a timed test.

Conditions: Following the previous test you will still be in the LYING POSITION, LOADED and READY. The test will start when you are ordered to "UNLOAD". Timing will be from the order "UNLOAD" until you have finished the UNLOAD. When finished, stand up, collect the ejected ROUND, inspect it and put it back in the MAGAZINE. Fasten your POUCH - time taken to fasten your pouch is not included in the time limit.

ASSESSMENT.

1. Standards: Skilled 12 seconds or less. Average - 13 to 18 seconds. Fail - over 18 seconds.

2. TWO seconds will be added to your time for each mistake made.

3. You will only pass this test if NO mistakes are made that affect SAFETY PRECAUTIONS or ACTIONS.

Skill at Arms & Shooting

TEST No 7 APPLICATION OF FIRE

Conditions: Using a figure target, your examiner will ask you to indicate on the target where your POI (POINT OF AIM) would be, as a result of two different questions he asks you relating to AIMING OFF FOR WIND at different strengths and ranges, and a third question on firing at a target crossing your front.

Examples of the questions are set out below:-

Question 1.

a. A fresh wind is blowing from Right to Left, the distance to the target is - 200 m, indicate your POA.

b. A strong wind is blowing from Left to Right. The distance to the target is - 200 m, indicate your POA.

Question 2.

a. A strong wind is blowing from Right to Left. The distance to the Target is - 300 m, indicate your POA

b. A fresh wind is blowing from Right to Left, the distance to the Target is - 300 m, indicate your POA.

Question 3.

As these tests can involve 'aiming off' the target area, you MAY have a second target to use for your POA indication.

a. Aiming at a Crossing Target, using the BASIC method, the distance to the target - 250 m, target walking.

b. Aiming at a Crossing Target, using the AMBUSH method, the distance to the target is - 80 m, target - running slowly.

ASSESSMENT.

Standards: Skilled - All correct. Average - two correct answers. Fail - Less than two correct answers.

REMEMBER - *PRACTICE MAKES PERFECT.*

Study these TRAINING TESTS, get them off 'word perfect', and then pitch your training to meet the needs of the tests.

Skill at Arms & Shooting

ANNUAL PERSONAL WEAPON TEST (APWT)

As a guide only, we set out in the following pages information and conditions of the APWT. Please check this information with your instructors as it may be subject to changes or variations.

The term 'Personal Weapon' is in fact the weapon you are issued with for operational purposes. You will also be expected to train on an 'Alternative Weapon' which is applicable to your particular Arm of Service, thus ensuring that in an emergency you have a 'second string to your bow'.

If you have an above average score in your APWT you could go on to qualify as a MARKSMAN. This will entitle you to wear the Marksman Badge - assuming it is authorised for your particular Arm of Service to wear them. Don't forget you will have to achieve the same good results the following year to keep your badge!

Your weapon training instructors will explain in detail the Practices, Ranges, Rules, Dress etc., that you will be required to comply with as a part of your APWT.

Essentially there are two 'Stages' or 'Phases' carried out by you in your shooting programme, as explained below:-

1. The first stage is the standard set for everyone to achieve as a recruit in their initial training.
2. The second stage is compulsory for the infantry and will be completed at the end of your special to arm training.

You will subsequently have to take the test every year. Members of other Arms and Service may complete their APWT as directed by higher authority.

Your 'Alternative' weapon already mentioned, requires that you are able to "handle and fire" the weapon safely, this is referred to as your Alternative Personal Weapon Assessment (APWA).

You will be tested on any of the practices from your previous tests - as applicable - and dependent upon the facilities and ammunition available at the discretion of your commanding officer.

FIRING REQUIREMENTS

1. *APWT*. Rifle APWT (TS) is to be fired by all soldiers during their Phase I All Arms Recruit Training. It is to be fired annually thereafter by all Other Arms and Service personnel whose personal weapon is the Rifle.

2. *APWA* Combat Infantry(CI) Practices number 2, 4, 8, and 9 may be fired by OA & Svcs soldiers who are equipped with LSW or the Pistol as a personal weapon.

Skill at Arms & Shooting

RANGES

Both the above tests can be fired on the ETR (Electronic Target Range), Gallery Range or Converted Gallery Range or Baffled Range. If the test is fired on a range converted to AMS the firing point monitors are NOT switched on.

TIMING

Each detail fired will take approximately 40 minutes to complete all practices.

RULES

1. Dress and equipment is Combat Dress, belt order webbing, combat helmet, combat body armour (where issued) and ear protection .
2. No extra time given for stoppages.
3. Coaching and signalling are not allowed.
4. Iron Sight only is to be used except for other arms and services soldiers whose personal weapon is the Rifle with SUSAT.
   SUSAT only is to be used.
5. If fire trenches are not available, prone position is to be used.
6. Practices 10 and 11 (Night Deliberate and Snap) may also be fired on the same occasion, and in addition to Rifle LF 14 (Firing at the Limit of Night Visibility (LNV).
7. Allocation of amunition for the APWA includes 20 rounds for registration, from which 5 rounds are to be fired at each range prior to the test shoot.

AMMUNITION

APWT(TS) 75 rounds. APWA (OA&Svcs) 50 rounds.
NOTE: The 50 rounds include 5 sighters brfore each practice

SCORING One point per hit.

STANDARDS:

APWT (TS) HPS 75 Pass 41 (52 using SUSAT) Marksman 60 (68 using SUSAT) To qualify as Marksman all Practices must be fired.

Marksman are eligible to wear the badge for 1 year before they must requalify.

APWA (OA&Svcs) HPS 30 Pass 21

Skill at Arms & Shooting

APWT - RIFLE

PRACTICE 1: SNAP

Range and Position adopted: 100m Sitting Unsupported.
Ammo: 5 rounds.
Target and Exposure:
a. Figure 12.
b. 5 x 4 seconds exposure with Irregular intervals.
Instructions: a. Firer in the nominated position.
b. Order ***"Watch and Shoot".***
c. On the appearance of the target, the firer is to fire one round at each exposure.
e. Targets fall when hit.

PRACTICE 2: SNAP

Range and Position adopted: 100m kneeling Unsupported/squatting.
Ammo: 5 rounds.
Target and Exposure:
a. Figure 12.
b. 5 x 6 second exposure with irregular intervals.
Instructions:
a. Firer in the standing alert position.
b. Order ***" Watch and Shoot"***
c. The appearance of a target is signal to adopt nominated position and fire one round at each exposure.
d. Between exposurers, order **"Stand up and adopt the standing alert position".**
e. Target fall when hit.

PRACTICE 3: SNAP

Range and Position adopted: 100m Standing unsupported
Ammo: 10 rounds.
Target and Exposure:
a. Figure 12.
b. 5 x double exposures
c. In each double exposure Targets up for 10 seconds, down for 3 and up for 5 seconds.
d. Irregular intervals between double exposures.

PRACTICE 3 SNAP (continued)

Instructions:

a. Firer standing alert position, 5m to rear of Firing Point.

b. Order ***"Watch out"***

c. Appearance of Target is signal to run onto the Firing Point, adopting nominated positionand fire ONE round at each exposure.

d. Between exposures ordered ***"Apply safety catches, dress back 5 m adopt the Standing Alert position".***

e. Targets fall when hit.

PRACTICE 4 SNAP

Range and Position: 200m, Prone

Ammo: 5 rounds.

Target/Exposure:

a. Figure 11.

b. 5x6 second exposure with regular intervals.

PRACTICE 5 SNAP

Range and Position. 200m Prone.

Ammo: 5 rounds.

Target/Exposure:

a. Figure 11.

b. 5x6 second exposures with irregular intervals.

PRACTICE 6 RAPID/SNAP

Range and Position adopted: 200m. Fire Trench.

Ammo: 10 rounds.

Target and Exposure:

a. Figure 11.

b. 1 x 10 second exposure, 15 seconds later, 5x6 second exposures with irregular intervals.

Instructions:

a. Firer in nominated position.

b. Order ***"5 Rounds Rapid, Watch and Shoot"***

c. Fire 5 rounds at the first exposure.

d. Target up and hold

PRACTICE 6 Instructions (continued)

e. After thr first exposure, order ***"Stop, Watch and Shoot"***

f. Fire ONE round at each of the remaining exposures.

g. Targets fall when hit.

PRACTICE 7: SNAP (NBC)

Range and Position adopted: 200m. Kneeling supported.

Ammo: 5 rounds.

Target and Exposure:

a. Figure 11.

b. 2 x 6 second exposure with irregular intervals.

Instructions:

a. Firer in nominated position, wearing Respirator and Gloves.

b. Order ***"Watch and shoot".***

c. Fire ONE round at each exposure.

d. Targets fall when hit.

PRACTICE 8: SNAP/ NBC

Range and Position adopted: 300m. Prone

Ammo: 5 rounds.

Target and Exposure:

a. Figure 11.

b. 5 x 6 second exposure with 5 second intervals.

Instructions:

a. Firer in the nominated position, wearing Respirator and Gloves

b. Order ***"Watch and Shoot"***

c. Fire ONE round at each exposure.

d. Targets fall when hit.

PRACTICE 9: SNAP/RAPID

Range and Position adopted: 300m Fire Trench.

Ammo: 10 rounds

Target and Exposure:

a. Figure 11.

b. 5x6 second exposures with irregular intervals, 15 seconds later 1x10 second exposure

PRACTICE 9: SNAP/RAPID (continued)

Instructions:

a. Firer in the nominated position.
b. Order ***"Watch and Shoot".***
c. Fire ONE round at each exposure.
d. Targets fall when hit.
e. After the fifth exposure, order
"Stop, 5 rounds rapid, Watch and Shoot"
f. Fire 5 rounds at the exposure.
g. Target up and hold.

PRACTICE 10: NIGHT SNAP

Range and Position adopted: LNV, Prone
Ammo: 5 rounds
Target/Exposure:

a. Figure 11 stick in (draped).
b. 5x6 second exposures with irregular intervals.

Instructions:

a. Firer in the nominated position.
b. Order **"Watch and Shoot".**
c. Fire ONE round at each exposure.
d. Targets do NOT fall when hit.
e. Record scores.

PRACTICE 11 NIGHT SNAP

Range and Position adopted: LNV Kneeling Unsupported.
Ammo: 10 Rounds
Target/Exposure:

a. Figure 11 stick in (draped).
b. 10x6 second exposures with irregular intervals.

Instructions:

a. Firer in the nominated position.
b. Order ***"Watch and Shoot".***
c. Fire ONE round at each exposure.
d. Targets do not fall when hit.
e. Record the scores.

Skill at Arms & Shooting

COMPETITION SHOOTING

Target Shooting is one of the very few sports that you are able to keep up throughout your life. After your time in the Army, Reserve Army or in fact any of the Services there are many Rifle Clubs throughout the country which you could join.

If you have been a good shot don't discard the skill, there are plenty of clubs and other organisations, especially the uniformed Youth organisations who would be glad to have your help, there is always something to look forward to with shooting.

It must be remembered that the success of most things we do, be it our job of work, a chore, a sport or a hobby, invariably goes to those who are both keen and determined to do what ever it is to the best of their ability.

This especially applies to shooting, where the amount of care and practice you have is directly related to the results you achieve.

No special skills are required, just keenness, practice and perseverance will bring you the rewards.

Competitions have always been used by the Army as a means of improving the standard of Marksmanship. The Boer War taught us a lesson in the need to have accurate riflemen in the face of overwhelming odds, as a consequence a period of feverish activity took place when Competition Shooting was the 'order of the day'.

The reputation the British soldiers had for their high standard of marksmanship during the initial fighting of the 1914-18 war, due to the continuous programme of Shooting Competitions that our regular and volunteer troops had taken part in prior to the war.

This standard of training was not maintained, as the newly arrived troops did not have time to be fully trained before being committed to battle. When they came 'out of the line' for R&R, those that were able, took part in shooting competitions to improve their skills.

Competitive shooting makes a valuable contribution as an integral part of your marksmanship training. If you are to keep up your standards in order to pass your Annual Personal Weapons Test (APWT), it makes good sense to get all the practice you can, what better way is there than holding down a place in your unit shooting team.

Shooting in the Regular Army and Reserve Army (TA) is split into two distinct activities; Qualification/Operational Firing and Skill At Arms Matches (under the control of the Army Rifle Association).

It must said at the outset that it is very difficult to try and treat them separately when you get down to the serious business of shooting skills.

Skill at Arms & Shooting

The reason being that many of the shooting principles generally apply equally to both Shooting as a Sport and Qualification /Operational Firing, because of this you may feel that they are both mixed up together.
The basic skills required are very much the same, but applied for a different purpose. We make no apologies about this; just ask you to bear it in mind throughout this Shooting Section.

It needs to be said at this juncture, that no units have an unrestricted supply of ammunition, and point out that it is just as much credit for you to be a Marksman with a .22 weapon as it is with the GPMG or the 5.56 Rifle in the context of maintaining your skill as a marksman.

What is important is for everyone to make good use of what range allocations and ammunition you do have available, for as many as possible to have the chance to take part in shooting on a regular basis.
It follows that if an opportunity presents itself to do some firing take every advantage of it to maintain and improve your own standards.
Perhaps the greatest difference between 'Shooting as a Sport' and 'Qualifying/Operational Firing' is that you have to be physically fit to carry out 'Qualifying/Operational firing' practices, as they involve practices running down the range or tactical firing on ETR ranges or Close Quarters Battle Ranges (CQBR).

Under the stress of firing in battle conditions, it is recognised that your shooting becomes erratic and below normal standards, not very good at a time when it needs to be well 'on target'. This form of stress can not be reproduced in normal training, but if you are a member of a team who get into a top competition , then the 'pressure will be on'. This provides a similar reaction to that of stress, and when you get down to fire 'shoulder to shoulder', you will quickly learn what 'competition stress' is all about.

The training you have to combat the stress factor should be to develop your personal skills in the determination to win as a member of the team. To build your self discipline giving you confidence in your own and the weapons ability and the concentration to bring it all together at the right time.

If you are a Recruit - a word of warning - don't be 'put-off' if at first you don't get a reasonable result. You must stick at it, as it is more than ever necessary in shooting. The reason being that your score suffers directly by the errors you make, there is no second chance, the mistake you make you pay for right away.

If you make less mistakes than the others - you will win.
Hopefully, this Skill at Arms section dealing with shooting will help you to:-

Skill at Arms & Shooting

1. Think positively about your training and what you could do to improve it.
2. Give you information and ideas for you to apply in your own training.
3. Improve your results, giving you more confidence in your ability.
4. Arouse your interest in pursuit of better results.
5. To pass on your skills to others who may be just starting to shoot.
6. Respect the patience and interest others have given to train you, and meet their expectations of you in return.

Once you start to improve - nothing will hold you back - only you can make the choice.
Don't miss a chance to have a practice shoot, no matter what type of weapon or range - PRACTICE MAKES PERFECT.

PERSONAL QUALITIES.

It is within the ability of almost anyone to become a good shot, provided they are 'mentally' and 'physically' fit. Mental Fitness -because it is to a great extent the 'mental control' that is required once you have learned the skills needed. The determination and keenness to succeed relies on Mental Fitness.
Physical Fitness in this context, is the need to have those parts of the body working sufficiently well to hold, sight and fire the weapon accurately.
Many firers find out - for the first time - that their eyesight is not as good as they imagined, have yours checked at regular intervals.
You will be constantly told that "your ability to shoot well depends entirely upon being able to GROUP TIGHTLY" or " you must have a good GROUPING capacity".
To explain this, imagine that perhaps the ideal method of holding and firing a weapon might be to have it clamped firmly in some device on the firing point - so as it cannot move, load and fire it at a target 100 metres away.
You may not believe it, but a weapon fired under these 'ideal' conditions would not put all the shots through the same hole in the target, it would produce shots spread out in a "GROUP".
It is not suggested that you can hold your weapon as firmly as some device, but firstly it is essential to learn to shoot when in the prone or lying position. The techniques and skills are dealt with later.

SKILL AT ARMS

DIAGRAM OF A 4ft TARGET ILLUSTRATING A "GROUP"

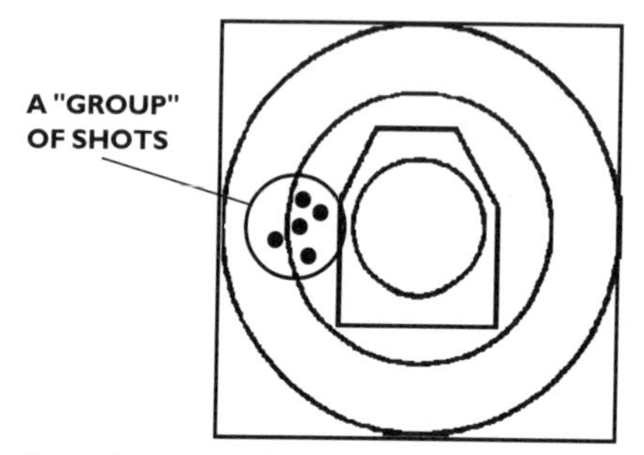

You will have been taught by your instructors how to handle the weapons SAFELY and to master the basic skills. Once you are qualified in these skills, then you will start to be given the training in some depth by coaching you for marksmanship during live firing practices. Your 'coach' will modify the techniques to suit your individual needs.

You will find that until you are able to achieve a satisfactory 'GROUPING CAPACITY', you will not be allowed to progress on to other practices. During your service the same will apply when taking your Annual Personal Weapon Test, if you are unable to group correctly, you will have to undergo remedial shooting training.

Your first objective must be to attempt to fire a group of five shots; having done this the second must be to concentrate on reducing the size (spread) of the shots in your first group, no matter how good it was, to an even smaller size.

On a .22 range of 25 metres should be firing a 1" group, once you have mastered this by getting it central on the target, then you are on your way.

GROUPING IS THE FOUNDATION OF ALL GOOD SHOOTING - UNLESS OR UNTIL YOU ARE ABLE TO ACHIEVE THE REQUIRED STANDARDS, IT IS DOUBTFUL WHETHER OR NOT YOU WILL EVER BECOME A MARKSMAN - MAKE EVERY ROUND COUNT

SKILL AT ARMS

RANGE MANAGEMENT

Every Range has their own set of Range Standing Orders, controlling all aspects of safety for those using the Range and the public at large. It is the responsibility of all units and personnel using the range to familiarise themselves with the range Orders.

Ignorance of Standing Orders is no defence. The most important action when first arriving in the vicinity of the Firing Point is that Safety Drills are carried out.

You will be inspected - your pockets and all personal equipment, webbing etc., will be checked to make sure that no DRILL ROUNDS are brought onto the Range.

Likewise, when finishing on the range for the day and just before you leave, you will be inspected again for any live ammunition or empty cases -even if you have been on the range in support of those firing as a working party.

At the actual time of your inspection by the Range Officer or Instructor you will make the following declaration to them, saying:- *"NO LIVE ROUNDS OR EMPTY CASES OR PARTS THEREOF IN MY POSSESSION, - SIR"* (that is assuming you DO NOT have any live rounds or empty cases lurking in your pouches - if you do - NOW is the time to produce them).

These and other Range Rules apply equally to all personnel on the Range, you will see your instructors and officers inspect each other in your presence.

MARKSMANSHIP PRINCIPLES.

The Definition of a Good Shot - What is Essential?

"To fire a shot without it disturbing your aim". To achieve this:-

1. The POSITION and HOLD must be FIRM ENOUGH to SUPPORT the weapon.
2. The weapon must point naturally at the target, without any undue physical effort.
3. The alignment of your sights and aiming must be correct. Sight adjustment and the SIGHT PICTURE must be correct.
4. You control the rhythm of your breathing and operate the trigger correctly.
5. The shot will be released and 'followed through' without undue disturbance of the position or your aim.

You must learn these Marksmanship Principles, until they become firmly established in your mind. The application of them demands great concentration on your part, this combined with the determination to be a Marksman will ensure your success.

SKILL AT ARMS

PRONE POSITION and HOLDING.

You must develop the control you have over HOLDING the weapon, to keep it steady. This is the foundation upon which to carry out the other activities, Viz BREATHING, AIMING, TRIGGER OPERATION, FOLLOW THROUGH.

Only when you have mastered the correct HOLDING will you start to improve upon your results. GET THE BASICS RIGHT - FIRST.

THE PRONE POSITION.

The prone position is the basic shooting position as it gives the firer the best support for the weapon, it is least tiring and presents the smallest image as a target to the enemy.

To maintain steadiness and be able to achieve a perfect hold, the first essential is that you are comfortable and feel that your weapon is a part of you. The importance of this cannot be over emphasised.

The position to be adopted on the ground, is with your body slightly oblique to the line of fire from which you are able to achieve the CORRECT AIM in the shortest time.

When getting on the ground hold the PISTOL GRIP with the Right hand, lie down, breaking your fall with the LEFT hand, keep the weapon parallel to the ground, make sure that no dirt get into the MUZZLE.

When you are down on the ground, tilt the weapon to the right, and support it by placing your LEFT hand under the HAND GUARD across the palm of your hand and hold with your fingers together. The grip should be no more than a stable platform for the weapon. NO attempt should be made to grip the HAND GUARD tightly or pull it backwards with the left hand. The position should be one of support.

The LEFT elbow is positioned as close as possible - in a comfortable position - to a point as near as possible, directly below the weapon. This position is intended to support the weight of the weapon on the bone of the arm, rather than using your muscular effort to support and hold it - which can't be sustained for very long.

You must be aware that this may produce a 'strained' position which is not comfortable for you, if so, you will not produce your best results, therefore adopt a comfortable position within the constraints of the correct hold.

SKILL AT ARMS

GET AND STAY COMFORTABLE.

The BUTT should be in a position against the muscle between the shoulder point and the lower edge of your collar bone - it should not come into contact with the bone itself.

Your RIGHT hand is the controlling hand and is the most important factor in good shooting. It should be high up on the PISTOL GRIP, with the web of the skin between thumb and forefinger positioned at the back of the PISTOL GRIP.

The grip must be firm, pulling back into the shoulder, but take care NOT to twist the weapon causing the SIGHTS not to be upright.

The first joint of your forefinger should be naturally on the TRIGGER.

The position of the RIGHT ELBOW is determined after taking the correct grip with your hand on the PISTOL GRIP. Your elbow also helps to keep your right shoulder in the correct position all the time.

Your body should be slightly at a angle to the 'line of fire', and your muscles in a relaxed state.

As you may not be accustomed to regular visits to the range, you may find it difficult to relax as there is always a certain amount of excitement in shooting. However in spite of this it is a part of the Self Discipline that you will need to master every time you get down to fire, BE - COOL - CALM, and COLLECT your THOUGHTS.

Your LEFT leg should be in line with your body, your RIGHT leg is positioned to form a continuation of the line of fire. Relax your leg muscles and turn your toes outwards with your heels on the ground. This position gives you the maximum amount of contact between your body and the ground, affording the most comfortable position.

This often puts extra pressure on your chest in contact with the ground. It can affect your breathing rhythm and you may feel that it restricts your breathing. If this is so, bend your right knee and bring your leg up slightly. This will raise the right side of your body just enough to make your breathing easier.

Keep your head in an upright position, this is its natural position used instinctively to maintain your sense of balance, and to correctly position your eyes immediately behind the sights.

Don't press your cheek hard against the CHEEK PIECE of the BUTT. Rest it lightly in a position that is comfortable and that you can keep for the time you are firing a practice. Don't get your eye too near to the BACK SIGHT. The distance should never be LESS than 25mm away.

SKILL AT ARMS

AUTOMATIC ALIGNMENT WITH THE TARGET.

The Marksmanship Principle - "that requires the rifle to point naturally at the target" needs little explanation as you will know how to adopt the correct firing position, but, if you are in a position that you have to strain even the smallest muscle to achieve the CORRECT AIM PICTURE it can affect your results.

At the moment you fire your weapon it will move against or be affected by that 'small muscle strain'. This strain is in force at the very moment you fire, in fact before the round leaves the MUZZLE of the weapon, the weapon will move against this strain and as a result your correct aim will be "off" and your results affected.

On firing it cannot be helped that your weapon will move, but natural alignment will go a long way to ensure that the movement is kept to a minimum.

Once you have had some experience of firing it will become easier for you to get into a correctly aligned position each time you fire. Until that time arrives you will have to practice 'testing and adjusting' until you find the most 'comfortable position'.

A useful tip to help find a 'comfortable position' is to shut your eyes and come up into the aim. As your eyes are shut you will instinctively adopt the most comfortable stance.

On opening your eyes, the AIM PICTURE should be on or very near the POINT OF AIM (POA) you had. If not your position should be altered.

Other ways to adjust your position are as follows:-

Aim at the target and then relax your hold. You should not notice any great change in your aim.

If there is, then it is an indication that you need to adjust your position.

If you need to correct lateral - LEFT to RIGHT errors. Keep your left elbow still, move your body slightly to the LEFT or RIGHT into the error as required.

To correct VERTICAL errors, keep BOTH your elbows still, and lift your body slightly forward or backwards - into the error - as required. Keep your BUTT in the same position in your shoulder.

The more you practice, it will become second nature to automatically adopt the correct position without a great deal of adjustment, but you should still go through this procedure every time you get down to fire.

SIGHT ALIGNMENT - AIMING

The CORRECT AIM PICTURE requires several different actions to be carefully coordinated at the same time, not just once, but time after time using exactly the same formula on each occasion. It is a lot to ask of our human make up to perform this, that is why you have to practice and have the patience to develop the skill.

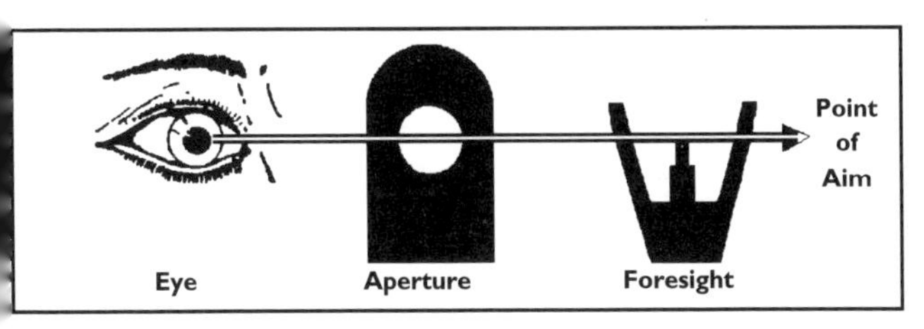

To achieve this CORRECT AIM PICTURE you have to align:-
1. Your EYE.
2. The CENTRE of the APERTURE BACKSIGHT.
3. The CENTRAL POINT of the TIP of the FORESIGHT.
4. Place the sights - so aligned on the POINT of aim on the target. See diagram above.

The correct focusing of your eyesight is essential to carry out the aiming. It is important to understand that you are asking your eyes to focus on two objects at different distances both at the same time.
The objects are the TARGET, or the TIP of the FORESIGHT.

FORESIGHT.

The critical part of SIGHT ALIGNMENT is the connection between the BACK SIGHT APERTURE and the FORESIGHT. Any errors you make are multiplied in proportion to the range of the target, so it is most important to make sure that the FORESIGHT is in clear focus at the moment of 'SHOT RELEASE'.
The tendency is to focus on the target and in so doing draw your attention away from the connection there should be between the FORESIGHT and the APERTURE BACKSIGHT. With sufficient practice and experience your eye will automatically line up the centre of the APERTURE in the BACKSIGHT, BUT, don't get carried away by thinking this does not need regular practice and concentration - it does!.

SKILL AT ARMS

CHARACTERISTICS OF THE WEAPON.

Particularly in Competitive shooting, the ability to fire your weapon and for it to produce a 'GROUP' of shots within a certain specified maximum area, is the essential requirement for you and your weapon to achieve .
You have to have complete confidence not only in your own capability, but also your weapons ability to achieve this goal. Once this confidence is achieved the weapon becomes an extension of your body.

TESTING YOUR INDIVIDUAL WEAPON.

A short range is better to test weapons, 30 or 100 metres - they are not affected by errors due to the wind. Check that the weapon you are about to use is in fact *'your weapon'*.
Ensure that the Barrel and CHAMBER are dry cleaned for firing.
Check that the weapon is functioning correctly, and if appropriate, that the magazine is correctly filled.
A Grouping Practice of five or more rounds should then be fired at any type of target having an easily defined Aiming Mark.
Should you make a faulty shot, this should be declared to your coach.
Weapons of the same type often have slight variations when fired, also the weather conditions, wind etc, may have to be taken into consideration as it can effect how your weapon fires. With practice under a variety of conditions, you will get to know how your weapon performs and become accustomed to its own characteristics.
Having spent considerable time with your weapon and come to terms with it and the results you are able to 'jointly' produce, what now can be done to improve your results?.
You must develop the control you have over HOLDING the weapon, to keep it steady.
This is the foundation upon which to carry out the other activities, Viz:
BREATHING, AIMING, TRIGGER OPERATION, and FOLLOW THROUGH.
Only when you have mastered the correct HOLDING will you start to improve upon your results.

GET THE BASICS RIGHT - FIRST.

You will also find out that the benefits of good holding will become more apparent when you are firing Rapid and Snap shooting practices.

CONTROL OF BREATHING.

We all breathe naturally at a steady rate with very little change in the rate of the number of breaths we take per minute, it has a natural rhythm - that is UNLESS we do something to upset it and it takes very little to do just that. Operational Shooting Practices invariably involve running down the range. You will experience that when you are out of breath - no matter how fit you are -that it is more difficult to concentrate on what you are doing. When you come up into the aim, your sights are not in focus, in fact may be blurred. You are far from being steady - never mind getting the right AIM PICTURE.

The reason for this is a lack of oxygen in the blood stream. It must be rapidly replaced by CORRECT BREATHING, which in turn reduces the tension and strain, allowing you to get back to the normal rhythm of breathing in the shortest possible time.

You will now appreciate that it is very important to keep your breathing under control when you are shooting. The need to be 'cool - calm - and collected' especially when leading up to the point at which you actually make the decision to fire the shot.

To assist you in this refer to the diagram below and the notes. Practice the timing for 'Breathing for Firing' as shown in the diagram until it becomes second nature, then apply it when you are shooting.

THE BREATHING CYCLE

There are three stages in the normal breathing cycle that are important to consider when shooting.

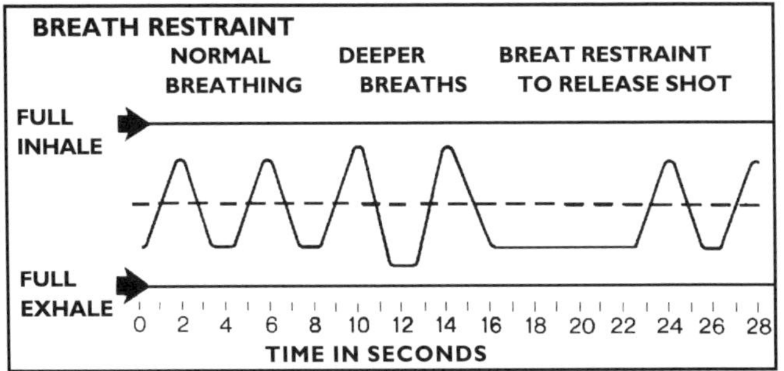

1. During normal breathing your lungs are neither completely filled nor emptied.
2. When breathing out there is a natural pause.
3. The time for the whole 'cycle' takes about five seconds. It is plain to see that the ideal time to fire a shot will be when your body is having a natural pause in the breathing cycle. The idea is to slightly extend that pause by a second, to six seconds.

TRIGGER OPERATION.

During the six seconds of BREATH RESTRAINT you have to perfect the CORRECT AIM and correctly operate the trigger so as to release the shot without any alteration to your aim or the grip with your Right hand.

To achieve the CORRECT SHOT RELEASE :-

1. Put your SAFETY CATCH to **'F'**.
2. Place your finger naturally on the TRIGGER.
3. Take a few slow deep breaths, at the same time take up the TRIGGER SLACK.
4. Hold your breath, PERFECT THE AIM, at the same time steadily apply increasing pressure to the TRIGGER until the weapon fires.
5. Maintain the pressure on the TRIGGER after the shot is released and concentrate on the AIM PICTURE until the weapon has settled; this is known as the 'FOLLOW THROUGH'.
6. Release the TRIGGER and continue to breathe normally. If for some reason you decide not to fire, relax and start again.

REMEMBER: This can only be achieved by the independent movement of the TRIGGER FINGER whilst the remainder of your body is perfectly still.

There are several different name given to the control of the trigger, Viz; 'let-off', 'final-pressure', 'trigger-pressing', 'trigger-squeezing'.

You may call it what you will, the fact is that - all trigger control is dependent for its efficiency on GOOD HOLDING.

No amount of super efficient 'trigger squeezing' etc., will make up for bad holding - REMEMBER - HOLDING is the FOUNDATION of good shooting.

Should you be involved in a long period of firing there is no doubt that some form of fatigue will become apparent. Usually you will notice that your eyes become tired, especially if you are inclined to remain in the aim too long.

As your eye gets tired its power of clear vision rapidly reduces. It can become upsetting if your results become erratic.

This is when it is important for you to strictly control the amount of time that you allow yourself for firing the number of rounds in each practice. Once you are in the aim - discipline yourself to get off your shots in say, the space of ten seconds - dependent upon your individual skills, preference and the conditions of the practice.

This approach will have its rewards when you fire Rapid or Snap Shooting practices. It is better to take a more leisurely approach, come down off the aim and start again. While out of the aim, relax and give your eyes a rest. It is always said that to look at the grass near to you on the range is good for the eyes, green being a restful colour.

Don't look down the range or at distant objects as your eyes have been accustomed to being focused on near objects such as your sights, therefore look at objects close by.

THE FOLLOW THROUGH

It is possible that you may respond to TRIGGER action or other influences at the very moment the weapon is fired and the BULLET is still in the BARREL. This can cause a shot to be misplaced, even so, it is essential that the shot is 'followed through' to the target. It requires you to concentrate during the period of TRIGGER operation and SHOT RELEASE.

As the shot is fired, the TRIGGER must be held to the REAR, keep your eyes open and look out for any movement of the FORESIGHT. This movement is usually in an upwards direction.

Remain still until the weapon has settled down. If your HOLD and POSITION are correct your SIGHT will normally settle on to the POA (Point Of Aim). Afterwards, continue to breath normally. If for some reason you decide not to fire, come off the aim, relax and start again.

ERROR RECOGNITION.

This aspect of shooting is especially important when taking part in your early training, but just as important in competitive shooting. When firing your practices on the range you should have an experienced shot with you as a 'Coach', who will be down by your side on the firing point.

The 'role' of the coach is essentially to watch over you and what you are doing to help and encourage you to carry out the actions and drills, safely and correctly as you have been taught, and to watch for faults in your technique and record your shots.

In advanced competition shooting you will come to rely on your coach for advice on matters such as changes in the wind and sight corrections.

When firing a shot there is some RECOIL ACTION produced by the

explosion of the round in the breech and the BULLET leaving the MUZZLE, plus the reaction of the weapons mechanism.
Assuming you are HOLDING the weapon correctly, the direction and amount of the weapons movement should be limited, then the position of your shots in the GROUP should be within your normal GROUPING CAPACITY.
If you concentrate on your AIM PICTURE each time you press the TRIGGER you will be able to see which way the weapon moves. As a result of this IF you do NOT HAVE a correct AIM PICTURE at the time of firing, you will immediately be aware that the shot will be outside your normal GROUP.
During practices on the range this has special significance as, when you realise that you have made an error you 'declare' it to your Coach by telling him that the shot has gone "low right" etc. If it was a genuine mistake - then it should not happen again - should it !

THE SLING - AN AID TO GOOD SHOOTING.

It is a matter of preference but many of the 'Top Shots' in the world who shoot at Bisley use a sling. Its purpose is in support of the weapon.
Current thinking favours the use of a SINGLE POINT SLING, where it is attached to the weapon at the fore end, leading over the wrist to a point high on the left arm well above the elbow.
This helps to keep the LEFT arm vertical under the weapon and does not exert any sideways pressure.
Some firers may prefer the TWO POINT SLING, where it is secured at the fore end and on the butt, they make the point that it gives more stability - especially in the wind. In the end it is a matter of choice which one you prefer, the important point to remember is that no matter which you use, it must be kept well up on your left arm or it will become uncomfortable and cause havoc with your shooting.
Having accepted that you are happy with a sling as an aid to your shooting, you will have to check it each time you use it, to ensure that it has been adjusted correctly, giving you the support that is comfortable to shoot with. If you share the sling with other firers, mark the settings for your own use to make sure it fits you next time.

CARE and CLEANING.

This subject has already been dealt with is some detail, but it must be emphasised that your CARE and CLEANING when you are involved in competitive shooting must be meticulous.

This extra care of your weapon may reveal something that could put you out of the competition - if you had not found it. It will pay dividends to be extra careful with all aspects of Care and Cleaning.

SHOOTING RECORDS

It is important to maintain your own Shooting Records in order that you see the progress you are making and to highlight those areas or practices that you need extra training or shooting practice.
If you do not keep a record it will be an indication of your lack of interest in keeping up your standards, which in the long run will make it more difficult for you to pass you APWT.

ABOVE ALL - CARRY OUT YOUR SKILL AT ARMS AND SHOOTING - SAFELY.

TEST QUESTIONS

1. Name four types of fire
2. Firing at a crossing target, what do you understand as "Lead"
3. Name three methods of engaging direct or oblique targets
4. Why is it NOT a good idea to fire from the hip
5. Name the seven training tests
6. What do you understand by "Personal Qualities" to aid good shooting
7. What do you understand as your "Grouping Capacity"
8. What controls ALL aspects of safety on any range
9. What and when are the safety drills carried out on the range
10. What is the personal declaration you and ALL others make on arrival and before leaving a range
11. What is the definition of a good shot and how is this achieved
12. In the Prone Position what helps you to sustain good results
13. What do you understand when shooting to get and stay comfortable
14. What is the definition of the correct "Aim Picture"
15. Being coached on the range, you make a faulty shot, what do you do.
16. What do you understand by "Breath Restraint"
17. When breathing what is the ideal time to fire a shot
18. What do you understand by "Correct Shot Release"
19. All Trigger control is dependent on its efficiency on ....
20. What do you understand by the "Follow Through",
21. How many AWPT's are there

The **Army Rifle Association** (ARA) is the official body, based at the National Shooting Centre, Bisley, which is responsible for the policy and organisation of all competition shooting with Service Weapons in the Army, world wide, and all the disciplines of the authorised Army sport of Target Shooting.
It also co-ordinates all match conditions to ensure they keep in step with current tactical doctrine, and maintains a close liaison with the other Services and National and International shooting organisations.

Central shooting matches are organised by units, Corps, Commands, Divisions and Districts at Skill-at Arms Meetings (SAMs). Regular and Territorial Army Teams and Regular Army individuals qualify from these Command/Division/District SAMs to compete in their respective central meetings held during the Central Skill-at-Arms Meeting (CENTSAM) at Bisley in late June/early July each year.

The overall individual Champion Rifle Shot in both the Regular and Territorial Army events wins Her Majesty The Queen's Medal for Shooting Excellence. A most prestigious and highly sought after award.

CHARTER

FOUNDED IN 1893

1. The Army Rifle Association (ARA) is an official body under the command of the Director of Infantry. The ARA is responsible to the Assistant Chief of the General Staff, through the Director of Infantry, for the management of Service Competition Shooting in the Regular Army and through the Director The Army Sport Control Board to the Adjutant General for the management of Target Shooting.

2. The aim of Service Competition Shooting is to promote interest in small arms shooting for Service purposes by means of individual and collective competitions, framed to include practice in methods, which will lead to increased efficiency on the battlefield.

Service competition shooting emphasizes the importance of accuracy with Service small arms. It also provides the soldier with an element of excitement and incentive to achieve success in conditions of tension, comparable in some degree to battle stress. From such experiences soldiers gain pride and confidence in their ability to handle their personal weapons to full effect.

3. Target Shooting is an authorized Army sport. Participation in local, national and international target shooting events keeps the Army in touch with developments in shooting techniques and provides units with expert coaches.

4. The Army Rifle Association origins date back to 1874 with the formation of two organisations - the Army VIII was formed to run central competitions, and the Inter-Regimental Rifle Matches were organized on a non-central basis. In 1893 these organisations were amalgamated under the aegis of the newly formed Army Rifle Association.
The Association remained a semi-official body supported by subscriptions and entry fees up to 1974, when it became an official organisation, part of the then Army Training Directorate.
However, the ARA retains its charitable status, with a Board of Trustees, and the financial affairs of the Association are in the hands of a Finance and General Purpose Committee under the Chairmanship of the Vice President.

5. Although the ARA is part of an MoD department, its shooting activities still have to be financed largely from entry fees.

6. Full details of the rules and matches of the Army Rifle Association are contained in Infantry Training Volume IV, Pamphlet No 20, Competition Shooting (All Arms) (Army Code No 71062 Revised 1997 including Amdt 4

SAM COMPETITONS

OUTLINE OF ARA MATCHES

In the following pages we give you brief details of the many Matches that the ARA are responsible for organising and controlling. You will appreciate the amount of administration and planning required to bring together vast numbers of competitors for the various Skill at Arms Meetings held each year. If you are taking any part in these events remember that when information is asked for by a certain date it is very helpful if you respond as requested.

MATCH 1

THE SERVICE RIFLE CHAMPIONSHIP FOR HM THE QUEEN'S MEDAL

The Service Rifle Championship is open to Regular Army Officers and Soldiers who have qualified through their Command, Divisional or District Skill at Arms Competitions.

Conditions

The aggregate score of Matches 2, 3, 4, 6, 7, 8 and 17.

MATCH 2 (ETR/AMS)

THE ROUPELL CUP

Outline of the Match

The match in fired in four practices, testing positional shooting at ranges from 100 to 300 metres at fleeting targets. It includes an NBC practice.

Conditions

Practice 1 – The Follow Up:

Practice 2 – Defence:

Practice 3 – Opportunity Targets:

Practice 4 – Close Quarter Battle:

MATCH 3 (CGR/AMS)

THE HENRY WHITEHEAD CUP

Outline of the Match

The match is a continuous fire and movement practice fired in four practices. The start line is the 500 firing point and bounds are as follows:

MATCH 3 (continued)

Bounds	Firing Point	Practice
1st	400 yards	1
2nd	300 "	2
3rd	200 "	3
4th	100 "	4

Conditions

Ammunition. Forty rounds in three magazines, one of 20 and two of 10 rounds each. Any number of shots may be fired at each exposure except in Practice 4. The firer is responsible for changing magazines when necessary

Practice 1 – Attack.

Practice 2 – Consolidation.

Practice 3 – Patrol Encounter.

Practice 4 – Close Quarter Battle.

MATCH 4

THE ASSOCIATION CUP

Outline of the Match

The match is a test of precision marksmanship at longer ranges, in varying positions and including fire and movement practices.

Conditions

Practice 1 – Sharpshooting:

Practice 2 – Fire and Movement:

Practice 3 – Rapid Fire:

Practice 4 – Snap:

MATCH 6 (MOVING TARGET)

THE WHITTAKER TROPHY

Outline of Match

The Match is an individual short range rifle match fired at a series of Fig 20 targets moving in different directions and speeds.

MOVING TARGET
Fig 20

A = Height 1365mm (app 4'6")
B = 610mm (app 2')
C = 260mm (app11")
D = 560mm (app 22")
E = 280mm (app 12")

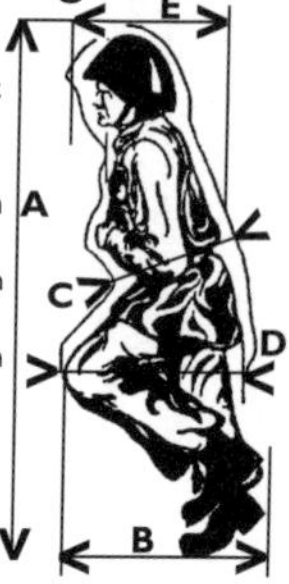

MATCH 7 (ETR)

THE ROBERTS - PRACTICE I

Conditions

Match 7 Practice I is a continuous match in three phases.

Practice I will reshoot the entire practice at the earliest opportunity.

Ammunition. Firers carry two magazines of 20 rounds and one of 10 rounds. After the first order to load a magazine of 20 rounds, firers will be responsible for changing magazines without further orders.

Phase I – Attack and Reorganisation:

Phase 2 – Counter Attack:

Phase 3 – Patrol Encounter:

MATCH 8

THE ARMY HUNDRED CUP

Outline of the Match

This is the final event of the Senior Rifle Championship and is restricted to the top 100 shots (aggregate score of the other Matches in Match I)

The match is a test of precision marksmanship in varying positions including fire and movement practices.

Practice I – Timed Harassing Fire

Practice 2 – Rundown

Practice 3 – Snap

Practice 4 – Rapid

Practice 5 – Snap

SAM COMPETITONS

MATCH 17

THE GRAHAM TROPHY (FIBUA)

Outline of the Match

The match is an individual short range rifle match to be fired under conditions likely to be encountered fighting in built up areas. There will be no sighters for the match.

Practice 1 – Firing from Cover (Snap).

Practice 2 – Firing around Cover (Snap).

Practice 3 – Snap.

Practice 4 – Snap.

MATCH 29

THE LMG/LSW MATCH

Outline of Match.

The match is a continuous fire and manoeuvre shoot in three phases to exercise a gunner in providing covering fire during an attack and defensive fire during reorganization. Competitors will be drawn up ten metres in rear of 600 firing point, ordered to load with 10 rounds and adopt the prone position.

MATCH 11 and 12

THE ARMY SERVICE PISTOL CHAMPIONSHIPS

General

The Service Pistol Championships is open to all Regular Army Officers and Soldiers irrespective of whether they have qualified to shoot in the QMC.

Outline of the Championship

The championship is to be fired in two stages:

SAM COMPETITONS

MATCH 11

Practice 1 – Covering Fire.

Practice 2 – Snap.

Practice 3 – Rapid.

Practice 4 – Close Quarter Battle.

Practice 5 – Continuous Fire and Movement.

A continuous fire and movement practice in four phases. The competitor is to have one magazine loaded with 13 rounds and the other with 7 rounds.

MATCH 12

Practice 1 – Initial Encounter

Practice 2 – Advance to Contact.

Practice 3 – Anti-Body Armour

Practice 4 – Close Quarter Snap.

Practice 5 – Close Quarter Attack

TEAM MATCHES

MATCH 28

MARCH & SHOOT (PARACHUTE REGIMENT CUP) (FIRE TEAM ASSESSMENT)

Outline of Match.

The match is a fire team fire and manoeuvre exercise testing the team's ability to put down effective fire whilst under physical stress, having completed an approach march of the type they may be required to perform on operations. The match consists of a continuous fire with movement exercise starting with an approach march of 2 miles to be completed in 20 minutes followed by six practices at ranges from 600 yards down to 100 yards.

Practice 1 – LSW/LMG Initial Contact.

Practice 2 – Fire and Movement.

Practice 3 – Winning the Fire Fight.

Practice 4 – Clearing the Position.

Practice 5 – The Counter Attack.

Practice 6 – The Follow-Up.

SAM COMPETITONS

MATCH 32

FIRETEAMMATCH

Outline of Match.

The match is a continuous fire team fire and manoeuvre shoot in four phases to exercise the team in a fire team attack and reorganization at ranges from 600 to 200 yards. The Fire team will be drawn up ten metres in rear of 600 firing point, ordered to load and adopt the prone position.

Phase 1 – Suppression of Enemy Position.

Phase 2 – Movement of Fire Team to FUP.

Phase 3 – The Assault and Clearing the Enemy Position.

Phase 4 – The Reorganization.

MATCH 34

COMBAT SNAPSHOOTING (THE BRITANNIA TROPHY)

Outline of Match

The Match is fired in two separate practices as follows:

Practice 1 – The Assault.

Practice 2 – Opportunity Targets (Snap)

The Team have to negotiate a series of obstacles before reaching the Firing Point and opening fire.
Score is based upon time taken to complete the shoot.

MATCH 37

THE FALLING PLATES MATCH

Procedure. The Match will be fired on a knock out principle with all byes in the first round. For all rounds prior to the quarter finals, four teams will run against each other, with one team going forward. From quarter finals onward two teams will run with one going forward.

SAM COMPETITONS

MATCH 39

THE PISTOL TILES MATCH

Procedure. The Match will be fired on a knock out principle with all byes in the first round. For all rounds two teams will run in each heat with one going forward.

INTERNATIONAL SERVICE RIFLE TEAM MATCH

Open to teams of 10 who are present members of the Regular or Reserve Armed Forces: one team from the United Kingdom and one team from each other country present whose national shooting organisation has been recognised by the NRA of Great Britain.

Outline of the Match

The match in fired in six practices, with 5 targets per team.

Practice 1 – Close Quarter:
Practice 2 – Brief Attack Encounter:
Practice 3 – Deliberate:
Practice 4 – Snap:
Practice 5 – Harassing Fire:
Practice 6 – Fire with Movement:

INTERNATIONAL SERVICE PISTOL TEAM MATCH

Open to teams of 8 who are present members of the Regular or Reserve Armed Forces: one team from the United Kingdom and one team from each other country present whose national shooting organisation has been recognised by the NRA of Great Britain.

Outline of the Match

The match in fired in five practices, with 4 Fig 11 targets per firer and four lanes per team.

Practice 1 – Covering Fire:
Practice 2 – Advance to Contact:
Practice 3 – Close Quarter Snap:
Practice 4 – Close Quarter Attack:
Practice 5 – Continuous Fire and Movement.

A continuous Fire and Movement practice in four phases.
The competitor is to have one magazine loaded with 13 rounds and the other with 7 rounds.

SAM COMPETITONS

MATCH 40

THE METHUEN CUP

Special Team Service Rifle Match. Conditions as for Match 8.

Introduction

1. This match originated in two triangular matches in 1894 and 1895 between teams from HMS Excellent, the Royal Marine Artillery and the School of Musketry, Hythe. After the 1895 match a meeting was held at which it was agreed to hold an annual match and to purchase a cup, towards the cost of which HMS Excellent, Royal Marine Artillery, Royal Engineers, Brigade of Guards, Green Jackets and the School of Musketry contributed. The late Field Marshal Lord Methuen, the GOC Home District presided at that meeting and the match was named after him. Subsequently other teams came in, each paying an affiliation fee as a contribution to the expenses of the match.

2. At first the match had its own separate organisation, but since 1900 it has been administered by the Army Rifle Association. The Badge is the same as that which, prior to 1890, was awarded to the 'Inter Regimental Rifle Match'.

Open to

Teams of a Captain and 6 firers from Commands of the Royal Navy and Air Force, Corps and Divisions of Infantry of the Regular Army, and to teams representing the Reserve Forces (TA) on payment of a separate entry fee. There is an alongside match for Overseas Teams.

Full details of the rules and matches of the Army Rifle Association are contained in Infantry Training Volume IV, Pamphlet No 20, Competition Shooting (All Arms) Army Code No 71062 Revised 1997 including Amdt 4

THE GENERAL PURPOSE MACHINE GUN (GPMG) (Light Role).

The GPMG provides the main fire support for the Infantry section and is used throughout the British Armed Forces in many and various roles which include an anti-aircraft role demonstrated during the Falklands conflict where it increased the protection given to the ships of the task force.

The GPMG is a 7.62 mm calibre, belt fed, bipod mounted, fully automatic, gas operated, machine gun which is capable of fast accurate fire to ranges up to 800m in the light role and up to 1800m in the Sustained Fire (SF) role.

Note, however that the SF role requires the addition of a tripod, different butt and a dial sight for recording targets.

These notes deal only with the light role.

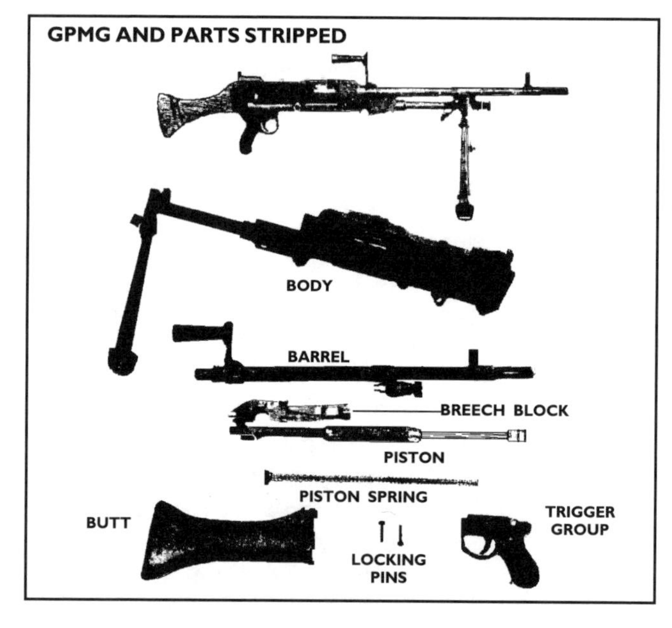

SAA GPMG

NOTE - Carry out NSP's (NORMAL SAFETY PRECAUTIONS) before starting any lessons with a weapon and at the end.

NORMAL SAFETY PRECAUTIONS

Kneel behind the gun, grasp the pistol grip with the left hand, open the top cover by pushing in the cover catches with the right hand, cock the gun by pulling the cocking handle fully to the rear, lift the feed tray.
Look inside and inspect the chamber and body to ensure they are clear, lower the feed tray and close the top cover. Hold the cocking handle with the right hand, press the trigger and allow the working parts to go forward under control.
Close the ejection opening cover unless stripping is to follow at once.

STRIPPING, ASSEMBLING & CLEANING THE GPMG.

Stripping Sequence

1. Check the weapon as above to make sure it is safe.
2. Make sure the working parts are forward.
3. Remove the sling.
4. Remove the butt.
5. Remove the return spring, piston and breech block. It is usual to clean these parts and reassemble before going on to the barrel group.
6. Cock the gun.
7. Remove the barrel.
8. Unscrew the gas regulator and remove the collars, plug and regulator. These would now be cleaned and then reassembled. The trigger group can also be stripped and cleaned after firing.
9. With the working parts forward remove the retaining pin.
10. Remove the trigger group by pivoting the group slightly downward.

CLEANING

The GPMG is equipped with a Spare Parts Wallet (SPW) which contains cleaning materials and spare parts. The contents of the SPW are :-
Oil can. Cleaning rod in two parts. Bore cleaning brush.
Chamber cleaning brush. Cylinder cleaning brush.
Gas port cleaner. Clearing plug. Spare firing pin.
Combination tool. Spare extractor, stay and spring.
Spare link pin Piston and cylinder cleaning tool.
Two spare collars. Gas regulator cleaning tool.
The GPMG is prone to becoming clogged up with carbon due to the large number of rounds it fires.

SAA GPMG

The gas parts are particularly bad with the carbon becoming very hard and very difficult to remove however it must be removed so persevere and get several of the other members of your section or group to help you.

1 Assemble the chamber cleaning brush to the rod and clean out the chamber.
2 Clean the barrel with 100mm by 50mm (4 x 2 inches) flannelette inserting the pullthrough at the chamber end only and pulling in one motion.
3 When clean, oil the barrel using 100mm x 38mm (4 x 1 $^1/_2$ inches) flannelette.
4 Clean and oil the flash hider.
5 Put flannelette round the cylinder brush and using the rod clean out the cylinder from the front. Oil the cylinder.
6 Clean the rest of the gun with an oily rag.
7 Reassemble the gun setting the gas to 6 if the normal setting is not known.
8 Clean, check and re-pack the SPW.

Assembly sequence

1 Check the numbers on the breech block and the body.
2 Replace the piston and breech block into the body.
3 Insert and secure the return spring.
4 Replace the butt.
5 Insert the plug into the seating on the barrel.
6 Replace the collars,screw regulator fully home, then unscrew to No 6.
7 Check the numbers on the barrel and the body and that there is no obstruction in the barrel.
8 Replace the barrel (weapon should be cocked).
9 Ease springs.
10 To replace the trigger group check that the safety catch is at **"F"**, insert the pistol grip and replace the retaining pin.
11 When fully assembled test the gun by cocking it and pressing the trigger with the recoil mechanism under control.
12 Lastly close the ejection opening cover.

GPMG AMMUNITION BELT

Ammunition for the GPMG is issued already belted in 200 round liners. These belts are broken down into the required lengths by holding the rounds either side of the point of separation and twisting them in opposite directions.

Belts are usually broken down into 50's and distributed throughout a section for use when moving or can be left in 200's in their tins when used in defence. Belts can be rejoined, but should not be made up from used links except in battle situation.

THE GPMG SIGHT PICTURE

SIGHT SETTING

The back sight is used in the lowered position for ranges 200 to 800m in the light role and is raised for use at greater ranges in the SF role.

LOADING AND UNLOADING

The prone position is adopted for loading, straight behind the gun with the legs together and heels uppermost. Hold the pistol grip with the right hand with the forefinger lying outside the trigger guard, put the butt in the shoulder with your cheek on the butt, place the left hand - palm down - on the butt with thumb underneath. Get comfortable with both elbows on the ground, with the forearms forming an "A" shape.

On the command "LOAD":-

I Tilt it to the right
2. Open the top cover (right hand)
3. Pick up the ammunition belt and check that it is not loose or damaged with your (left hand)
4. Place the belt in the feed tray (left hand) with the first round against the cartridge stop and close the top cover (right hand).
5. Replace the hands in their correct positions
6. Hold the gun upright

On the command UNLOAD:-

1. Open the top cover by pushing in the cover catches but do not lift it.
2. Raise the butt into the shoulder and cock the gun
3. Lower the butt
4. Raise the top cover and remove the belt
5. Clear the feed tray of empty links
6. Close the top cover
7. Raise the butt into the shoulder align the sights and squeeze trigger.
8. Lower the butt
9. Close the ejection opening cover
10. Lower the sights and stand up.

Sometimes on the range you will be required to Clear the gun. To do this you should unload the gun then raise the top cover to its upright position, stand up and report "Gun Clear".

On the command "MAKE SAFE": unload, then reload but **DO NOT** cock the weapon.

Loading and Unloading with a two man team.

When a Number 2 is provided for the gunner he should lie on the left of the gunner and assist with loading and unloading.

To load, the gunner raises the top cover, the No 2 places the belt in the feed tray keeping his fingers clear of the top cover as the gunner closes it. During the unload the No2 removes the belt from the feed tray.

HOLDING AIMING AND FIRING

Although the GPMG rests on a bipod you must be able to hold the weapon, aim and fire in bursts against both stationary and moving targets.

Holding and Aiming

1 You will be given a range or the order to load.

2 Aiming is as for the rifle since the sights are of the same type.

3 To begin roughly adjust the weapon on to the target by placing the left hand under the weapon, lifting and moving the gun in line with target.

4 Adjust for height by moving the elbows apart or together or for large adjustments alter the nut between the bipod legs.

5 Move your shoulder firmly up to the butt of the gun.

6 Pull the butt into the shoulder, backwards and downwards with the left hand on the butt and the left elbow as far forward as possible.

7 Hold the pistol grip firmly with the right hand, forefinger over the trigger, and pull the gun backwards and upwards.

8 Lock the position by twisting the wrists against each other and rest the cheek on the butt/left hand.

9 To test your position rock backwards and forwards slightly; the foresight should move up and down on the point of aim.

SAA GPMG

FIRING

1. On the command fire and when you have finished adjusting, squeeze the trigger, holding it long enough to fire a burst of two or three rounds, then release the trigger without disturbing the position.
2. As soon you have fired, open both eyes and look for the fall of shot.
3. Make any necessary adjustments and then continue firing at a rate of 25 rounds per min or 100 per min if Rapid fire is ordered.
4. **When ordered to "STOP"**, cock the gun, put the safety catch to safe and rest the butt.
5. **When ordered to "GO-ON"**, aim and continue firing.
6. If a No2 is available he should keep the gun fed with ammunition by clipping on more belts and ensure that they feed into the gun correctly.

IMMEDIATE ACTION AND GAS STOPPAGES

IA drills for the GPMG are as follows. If the gun stops or fails to fire:-

1. Cock the gun.
2. Lower the butt.
3. Open the top cover, clear the feed tray and close the top cover again as quickly as possible.
4. Raise butt into the shoulder and align the sights then press the trigger.
5. Lower the butt, reload and carry on firing.

The following stoppages will be remedied by using the "IA":-

1. Expended belt.
2. Damaged rounds.
3. Poor feed.
4. Misfired round.
5. Hard extraction.
6. Damaged link.

If the gun cannot be cocked open the top cover, clear the feed tray, close the top cover and complete the IA.

GAS STOPPAGE DRILL

If after completing the **IA** the gun fires a few rounds and stops again do the following:

1. Cock the gun.
2. Put the safety catch to **"SAFE"**.

3. Lower the butt.
4. Adjust the regulator 3 clicks. If hot use the nose of a round in the holes in the regulator.
5. Put the safety catch to **"FIRE"** and carry on.

Do not try to reuse damaged rounds, put them to on side and hand them in after firing. If after carrying out the stoppage drill it recurs you should look closely at the rate of fire and cleanliness of the gun and either adjust or clean the gun.

OTHER STOPPAGES

Stoppages caused by broken parts are rare, however, they do sometimes occur and are usually due to the following.

1. An obstruction in the body, empty case in the chamber. Cleared by unloading, inspecting and removing the obstruction.
2. Broken parts, obstruction in the barrel, separated case. Cleared by unloading, inspecting, removing the obstruction and replacing any broken parts.
   A separated case will require the use of the clearing plug.
3. Feed pawl and springs. If after carrying out the IA the gun will not fire and you cannot fully cock the gun, inspect the feed pawls and springs to see that they are working correctly. You may have to clean and oil them before reloading.
4. Runaway gun. A mechanical fault may cause the gun to continue firing after the trigger has been released, if this happens hold the gun firmly into the shoulder and twist the belt at its point of entry to the feed mechanism to cause the gun to stop.

When the gun has stopped, reload, adjust for more gas, cock the gun and carry on firing.

GPMG TRAINING TESTS

The purpose of these training tests are to measure the standards that you have attained in safety and handling of the GPMG. You will be tested during your Recruit training and thereafter annually.

TEST No 1. SAFETY

Stores: Gun loaded, cocked and safety catch at SAFE. Gun either in the corner of a room or on the firing point.

Conditions: You will be ordered to bring the gun to the centre of the room, or to another position on the firing point. You should - without further directive - carry out the normal safety precautions on the gun.

ASSESSMENT: You will **FAIL** if the safety actions are not carried out correctly.

TEST No 2. STRIPPING, CLEANING & ASSEMBLING.

Stores: GPMG Weapon. Spare parts wallet complete. One 7.62mm Drill Round.

Conditions: You will be ordered to strip the gun as for daily cleaning. The following questions will be asked:-

1. What size of flannelette is used to clean the bore.
2. What size of flannelette is used to oil the cylinder.
3. What spare parts for the gun are contained in the section wallet. You will them be ordered to assemble the gun.

ASSESSMENT: Main purpose to assess your ability to strip and assemble the gun. You are assessed follows:- SKILLED made no mistakes. AVERAGE made 1 to 3 mistakes. FAIL made more than 3 mistakes.

NOTE. No qualification is awarded if any mistakes affect safety.

TEST No 3. LOADING.

Stores: GPMG Weapon. Belt of 15 DRILL rounds. Stop Watch.

Conditions: This is a TIMED TEST. You are tested lying behind the gun. Safety catch at FIRE. Belt on the ground on the left of gun. Ordered to LOAD. Time is taken from the time of the order LOAD, until you have both hands in their proper position on the gun and the gun is upright.

ASSESSMENT: SKILLED - 8 seconds or less. AVERAGE - 9 to 12 seconds. FAIL over 12 seconds.

NOTE. Two seconds are added to the overall time for each mistake. No qualification is awarded if any mistakes affect safety.

TEST NO 4. IMMEDIATE ACTION & GAS STOPPAGES.

Stores: As for TEST No 3.

Conditions: This is a TIMED test. You are tested lying behind gun, gun loaded and firing. Order GUN STOPS. When the IA has been done, order GUN FIRES A FEW MORE ROUNDS AND STOPS AGAIN.

Time taken from AGAIN until you have aimed and fired the gun. Mistakes made in the IA count for the test.

ASSESSMENT: SKILLED -8 seconds or less. AVERAGE - 9 to 10 seconds. FAIL - over 10 seconds.

NOTE: Two seconds are added to the overall time for each mistake. No qualification is awarded if any mistakes affect safety.

TEST No 5. UNLOADING.

Stores: As for TEST No 3.

Conditions: This is a TIMED test. You are tested lying behind gun, gun loaded and firing. Ordered to STOP and when actions have been carried out correctly, given the command UNLOAD. Time taken from the UNLOAD until you are standing up behind gun.

ASSESSMENT: SKILLED - 8 seconds or less. AVERAGE - 9 to 12 seconds. FAIL - over 12 seconds.

NOTE: Two seconds are added to the overall time for each mistake. No qualification is awarded if any mistakes affect safety.

TEST No 6. PREPARATION FOR FIRING.

Stores: GPMG Weapon. Spare Parts Wallet complete. One 7.62 DRILL round. Flannelette. Oil.

Conditions: You will be ordered to prepare gun for firing.

Without further direction you should:-

a. Strip the gun as for daily cleaning, clean and leave dry.

b. Open the dust cover, clean and oil the guide ribs then close the dust cover.

c. Oil the bearing surfaces of the breech block and piston extension, locking lever and locking shoulder, feed arm and feed channel, the return spring and the trigger mechanism.

d. Set the gas regulator at its correct setting, check there is no obstruction in the barrel and that it locks firmly into position.

e. Check sights for tightness.

f. Ensure ball of the firing pin is seated correctly in its recess.

g. When the gun is assembled, press the trigger and move the working parts backwards and forwards a few times

ASSESSMENT: The sequence used need not be the same as laid down in the conditions above, but all aspects are to be correctly completed.

SKILLED - Up to 2 mistakes. **AVERAGE** - 3 to 5 mistakes.

FAIL - Over 5 mstakes

NOTE: No qualification is awarded if any mistakes affect safety.

SAA GPMG

SELF TEST QUESTIONS

1. What is the calibre of the GPMG
2. GPMG in light role - what is the maximum range
3. How many rounds are issued in a GPMG ammunition belt
4. GPMG "Make Safe" what is carried out
5. GPMG what is the normal rate of fire and Automatic
6. GPMG - how do you stop a "Runaway Gun"
7. How many training tests are carried out for the GPMG
8. What range is the GPMG used in the 'light role'.
9. When is the GPMG mounted on a tripod
10. In the Sustained Fire role up to what range is the GPMG effective.
11. What is meant by the GPMG 'SF' Role. And what changes are made to the weapon to fire in the 'SF' Role.
12. Carrying out the NSP's what position do you take up with the GPMG.
13. Give the Stripping Sequence for the GPMG.
14. What does an MFC do.
15. Where will you find a 'beaten zone'.
16. What size 'flannelette' is used to oil the barrell of the GPMG.
17. What is the difference between Fig 11 and Fig 12 targets.
18. Name all the contents of the GPMG (SPW) Spare Parts Wallet
19. Why does the GPMG often become clogged up with carbon.
20. When reassembling the gun if you do not know the normal settring which setting would you use.
21. Under what conditions would you make up ammunition belts from used links.
22. Adopting the prone position behind the gun in what position are your heels.
23. When a number two is provided which side of the gun do they work.
24. Name the 6 stoppages that can be remedied by IA drills.

25 What is the easiest way to fail your GPMG Training Tests.

INFANTRY SUPPORT WEAPONS

CHARACTERISTICS OF THE 81 mm MORTAR

Fire-power Characteristics

Accuracy. The 81 mm mortar is a very accurate weapon. The sight system includes the Mortar Fire Data Computer (MFDC).

Consistency. Because of the very fine machining of rounds and the barrel, produces accurate fire comparable with a field gun.

Beaten Zone. The effective beaten zone of one section of mortars at maximum range is approximately 200 metres square. At shorter ranges and with lower charges the beaten zone is smaller.

Flexibility. The range varies from 180-5660 metres for HE and WP ammunition. The mortar can engage targets over a 6400 mils arc.

Ammunition. The mortar fires three main types of ammunition -High Explosive, White Phosphorus Smoke and Illuminating. The HE and WP matched charges. The illuminating ammunition has a range of 4050 metres, a burning time of 43 seconds, will illuminate area of 400 metres radius. The brightness is 400,000 candle power.

High Rate of Fire. The mortar can fire more than 20 rounds a minute; Under normal circumstances Rate 12 should be used; this will give from one to 12 rounds of fire in a minute.

Danger Area. The HE round has a high lethal capability up to a radius of 40 metres from the point of burst and it can be expected to cause casualties up to 190 metres from the point of burst.

Ability to Fire at Obscured Targets. The mortar has the capability of firing on previously adjusted targets when they are obscured by darkness, fog or battlefield smoke. Targets not previously adjusted can be engaged, but the fire will be less accurate.

Response Times. Being a battalion asset fire is guaranteed to the battalion. This often is not the case with artillery fire. Response times compare well with artillery. Their role in general is to give:

Final Protective Fire (FPF). If the mortars are laid on a target the time to have effective fire will be from 20-60 seconds.

Defensive Fire (DF). Approximately three minutes, and individual skill Is in the time of flight.

Time of Flight. This varies between 12 and 51 seconds.

INFANTRY SUPPORT WEAPONS

Deployment Characteristics

High Trajectory. The high trajectory enables it to fire from behind high cover. Engage targets in dead ground or defiladed from other weapons.

Ground. When firing the ground must be firm and stable. Very rocky ground and marshes must be avoided.

Mobility. Mortar detachment are self-contained, in a 1 tonne Landrover and trailer or FV 432.

Weight of Stores. The main parts of the mortar are light weight compared to the ammunition which is both bulky and heavy. Help is necessary for carrying ammunition.

Vulnerability. The mortar needs carefully located, preferably in dead ground. High trajectory, long flight time, easily recognised sound and muzzle flash make the mortar vulnerable to sound ranging, mortar-locating radar and visual detection.

Organization. At company level mortar fire is controlled by the MFCS. An MFC party consists of two MFCs and a driver. They are equipped with radios and optical devices, including SPYGLASS.

Allocation. Mortar sections are allocated at priority call to companies by the mortar platoon commander.

CHARACTERISTICS OF MILAN

General introduction.

MILAN is a second generation, semi automatic wire guided missile system. This means that after launch, the operator only has to track the target by keeping the cross hairs on it. He does not have to fly the missile as in older systems.

There are three main component parts:

a. The Firing Post - which contains the launch, tracking and guidance system.

b. The Missile - in its separate tube.

c. MILAN Infra-Red Adapter (MIRA) - a thermal imaging sight which forms an integral part of the system.

Range. When fired the missile is armed at 20 metres it can only be used in an emergency at less than 400 metres, because it is not until this range that the missile has settled onto its correct flight path. The maximum range is 950 metres

Accuracy. The system has a high degree of accuracy against all targets due to its semi automatic nature and to the operator's x7 magnification in the sight.

Effect on Armour The missile has a 115 mm HEAT warhead which will penetrate 352mm armour. It will penetrate the side armour of most known AFVS. It should be sited in defilade,

Concealment. MILAN's small size and low silhouette make it easy to conceal.

Handling. The firing post weighs 18 kilograms and the MIRA sight 7 kilograms. Both are carried by the MILAN operator. Each missile weighs approximately 12 kilograms and two missiles are carried by his No 2. Since MILAN is a relatively light, compact and robust system, ideal for airmobile and airborne operations.

Flexibility. MILAN can be used in the open or fired from a trench. It can be mounted on various vehicles such as the FV 432 , or in the MILAN Compact Turret mounted on SPARTAN (MCT(S)). The post has an all round traverse of 6400 mils.

Pre-Firing Checks. A simple visual pre-firing inspection is required on the MILAN ammunition tube. The firing post can be tested by the MILAN operator by using a simple 'GO/NO GO' Unit Test Equipment

Limitations

Time of Flight. The time of flight to maximum range is approx 12 seconds. This precludes the engagement of fleeting targets and it results in a slower rate of fire. It also requires the firer to be protected during the missile's flight.

Rear Blast Area. On launch the missile tube is ejected to the rear and there is a small back blast. A zone 5.5 metres behind, 533 mils either side of the axis and 0.5 metres above the level of the ammunition tube must be clear of men, equipment and obstacles.

Decoy. The Heat from a burning tank or building may decoy the missile if close to the flight path. The MILAN tracker confuses the battlefield IR source for the IR tracking flare on the missile. This can be partially overcome by experienced and well trained operators.

THE MINIMI SQUAD AUTOMATIC WEAPON {SAW}
C79 ELCAN OPTICAL SIGHT
CARRYING HANDLE
FORE SIGHT
FLASH ELIMATOR
BUTT STOCK
GAS TUBE
BIPOD MOUNTING POSITION
AMMO BOX MAGAZINE {BELTED AMMO}
ALTERNATIVE BUTT GRIP
Photo HQ Land Command

INFANTRY SUPPORT WEAPONS

THE MINIMI (SAW)

SQUAD AUTOMATIC WEAPON

The MINIMI Automatic Squad Weapon is manufactured in Belgium by Fabrique Nationale Herstal. Many different nations manufacture variants under licence and use their own reference numbers and names. One of the variants has a shorter Barrel and retractable STOCK for use by Para Units and other modifications making it user friendly.
It is envisaged that within an infantry section the MINIMI will eventually replace the LSW to provide covering fire during offensive action and could be paricularily useful in a defensive role.
It is unlikely that the MINIMI will take the place of the GPMG as the 7.62 mm GPMG longer range and power to lay down defensive fire. It is well proven weapon for mounting on vehicles and used as an anti aircraft weapon.
The MINIMI is lighter and more manoeuvrable than a GPMG and loaded with 200 rounds weighs about a kilo less than a 7.62 mm GPMG in the unloaded state.

A new ammunition type was develpoed for the MINIMI. NATO was also at this time conducting an Ammunition Standardisation Trial and selected a new 5.56 mm round.
The new M856 5.56mm tracer cartridge has a red colour tip. The tracer bullet has a burn-out distance of 900 metres.
The 200-round belts of 5.56 mm ammunition are issued either as loose belts or in a plastic pack with a ratio of one tracer round to four ball.

Belted ammunition is carried in a plastic box magazine fitted below the weapons receiver. Pouches carrying 200 rounds are available, there is a smaller one hundred round pouch if keeping the weight down is required.
Its rotary gas regulator is adjusted by hand. It has two positions normal turn to left and adverse turn to right.
The SAW gives the section fire team a light machine gun of greater all round capability than an assault rifle, without the weight of a .30 calibre weapon.
Loaded with 200 rounds the SAW weights 10 kg and is just over one metre long.
The main component parts of the Minimi have a service life of over 50,000 rounds. This is a crucial factor when you consider the high volume of ammunition that will be discharged by a machine gun engaged in combat operations.
The iron sights can be adjusted from 300 metres to 1000 metres in 100 metre increments.
They can also be adjusted from side to side to correct for crosswinds. Mounts are also available to attach day and night scopes and lasers.

Photo HQ Land Command

A bipod with adjustable leg height is fitted to the basic SAW and the Para model, and can be folded backwards to allow firing from the hip or for ease of transport.
The bipod can also be folded forwards when the weapon is fitted on a tripod mount. The trigger guard can be removed to allow the use of arctic or NBC gloves.
Other accessories include optical sight mounts, day and night scopes, a cleaning kit that fits into the handguard, a sling and a carrying bag for a spare barrel.

THE L115A1 .338 RIFLE

THE L115A1 Rifle which has been issued to specialist Army Units will greatly enhance the effectiveness of troops on the ground beyond the range and performance of their 5.56 Rifle/LSW.
It fires a .338 round with a range of 500m.The large-calibre *Super Magnum* is capability of disabling soft targets at 500m.
Currently issued to Joint Rapid Deployment Force and used at platoon level by the best shots.
This is considered to be a major asset available to the platoon commander who find themselves in need of heavy support where he may have previously had to call on supporting fire.

Photo HQ Land Command

The Rifle has a single-shot bolt action initially described a *sniper rifle,* the L115A1 is most likely to be used in taking out a specific target rather than being engaged in a fire fight..
The types of ammunition for the rifle, can be ball, armour-piercing and armour-piercing incendiary rounds (the "flash" of which indicates a hit. Demonstrations have shown that it can penetrate brickwork and steel plating during trials, firing was concentrated on a battle range of 800m, man-sized targets out to 1,200m and vehicles at 1,500m.
Those who have fired the weapon speak very highly about it saying that it is "comfort-able" and "user-friendly". It does not have the 'kick' or recoil associated with larger-calibre rifles.
A Schmidt und Bender 3-1 2x50 sniper telescope ensures the L115A1 accuracy at long ranges
The Simrad 200 series night sight provides additional benefits to the Platoon Commander.
It can be fired from the shoulder or from a steel bipod. The STOCK is made of reinforced nylon and designed for either left or right-hand shot The STOCK, folds away when on the move
It has made a very good impression on all who have used it and witnessed its capability. Although limited in its distribution it is felt that it will become a standard part of the Infantry Battalions assets.

GRENADE LAUNCHER

Photo HQ Land Command

Heckler and Koch have developed a Grenade Launcher known as the AG36.
The configuration of the launcher is that it is fitted under the Barrell of the 5.56 Rifle and has a separate Pistol Grip and Trigger.
Having this extra or added weapon will be of great advantage to the fire capability within the Infantry Section Fire Team.
The Infantryman will now be able to either fire his rifle or launch a grenade as and when required.
It is thought that the Grenade Launcher will be fitted to one 5.56 Rifle per section. The front end of the Rifle will be fitted with an adaptor to which the Launcher is attached.
A 'ladder' type apeture sight is fitted to the left side of the Launcher and is marked from 50 metres to 350 and is aligned with the foresight as in the normal 'aim picture'.
In loading the Launcher with a round it is tilted to the left for the 40mm round to slip in.
The types of 40mm ammunition are: armour piercing, high explosive, shotgun, and flare,
The pistol grip of the Launcher has a safety catch, marked 'S' and 'F'.
The weight is approximately 1.5 kilos.

SKILL AT ARMS & SHOOTING

SELF TEST QUESTIONS

1. What is the ARA and what are they responsible for.
2. When was the ARA founded
3. Explain the aim of Service Competition Shooting
4. Is Target Shooting a recognised Army Sport.
5. Back in 1874 what were the two organisations formed to run central competitions.
6. How are ARA activities funded to a great extent.
7. Where will you find the full details of the rules and matches of the Army Rifle Association.
8. What is a Figure 20 target used for.
9. In the Parachute Regiment Cup how far is the approach march and in what time to be completed followed by how many practices.
10. How many firers in a team for the International Service Rifle Team Match.
11. How did the Methuen Cup match originate and who started it.
12. What is the range of the 81mm Mortar from .....to ....
13. What types of ammunition does the 81mm Mortar fire.
14 The 81mm Mortar can fire more than .... rounds in a minute.
15. The time of flight of a Mortar round is between ... and ..... seconds.
16. How is the Milan Rocket guided on to it's target.
17. When fired the Milan Missile maximum range is ... and takes ..... seconds.
18. How are the 'pre-firing' checks carried out on the Milan.
19. When a Milan is fired, what do you understand about the rear blast area.
20. The Minimi Squad Automatic Weapon (SAW) fires what size round.
21. Belted Ammunition is carried in a plastic box . Where is it fitted.
22. The Minimi Iron Sights cab adjusted from .... to .... in increments of ....
23. The L115A1 .338 Rifle is a valuable asset for a Platoon Commander. Why.
24. What is the special feature of the L115A1 stock and what is it made of.
25. The Grenade Launcher (AG36) fires a .... mm round and what are the 4 different types of round it fires.

SHOOTING RECORD

Date	Weapon Fired	SUSAT No	Type of Practice Fired	Type of Range	HPS	Score or Group Size	Remarks

SHOOTING RECORD

Date	Weapon Fired	SUSAT No	Type of Practice Fired	Type of Range	HPS	Score or Group Size	Remarks

SHOOTING NOTES